Student Activity Guide

for

Parents and Their Children

by

Verdene Ryder
Family Life Education Consultant
Houston, Texas

and

Nancy Henke-Konopasek, CFCS
Senior Editor
Munster, Indiana

Publisher
The Goodheart-Willcox Company, Inc.
Tinley Park, Illinois

W9-BYB-338

Introduction

This activity guide is designed for use with the text *Parents and Their Children*. It will help you explore the decisions related to parenthood, the stages of child development, and many contemporary parenting concerns.

The activities in this guide are divided into chapters that correspond to the chapters in the text. The best way to learn the material is to first read your assignment in the text. Then do as much work in the activity guide as you can without turning back to the text. If necessary, you can look at the text again later to complete any questions you could not answer and to compare your answers to the information in the text.

You will find a variety of activities in this guide. Some of the activities, such as crossword puzzles, can be used as study guides as you review in preparation for quizzes and tests. Do your best to complete these activities carefully and accurately. Other activities will ask for opinions, evaluations, and conclusions that cannot be judged as right or wrong. The object of these activities is to encourage you to consider alternatives and to evaluate situations thoughtfully. The text will be a useful reference in completing these activities.

The activities in this guide have been designed to help you gain as much as possible from your study of parenthood and child development. It is to your advantage to give thoughtful consideration to each response you make. The more thought you put into the activities, the more knowledge you will gain from them.

Contents

Part Two
The Beginning of Parenthood

Part Three
Understanding Children's Growth and Development

● **Part Four:
The Challenges of Parenting**

1 Parenting as a Career

Parenting Job Qualifications

Activity A

Chapter 1

Name _____

Date _____ Period _____

Some of the qualifications required for the job of parenting are listed below. Read the qualifications. Then use them to complete the parenting job description profile on the following page by listing each qualification in the appropriate column. You may add additional qualifications if you wish.

Parenting job qualifications:

Health care provider — Maintains proper schedule of rest and exercise for children. Sees that children have the proper vaccinations. Can identify the symptoms of illnesses, perform first aid, and obtain medical services if needed.

Nutrition provider — Provides nutritious foods at properly scheduled feeding times. Is aware of the nutritional needs of children as they develop.

Teacher — Provides an enthusiastic attitude toward learning activities. Recognizes the value of providing children with lessons that will enrich their lives and sharpen their awareness of the world around them, other cultures, and their heritage. Also, promotes moral development.

Assistant decision-maker — Is able to help children make decisions. Assists children in the decision-making process, but allows children to arrive at their own decisions.

Communicator — Is able to let children know they are loved through both word and touch. Is able to speak to children in a pleasant manner, rather than in a bossy, demanding tone.

Resource person — Answers children's questions. Is able to read the same book over and over again without showing boredom.

Social director — Provides social activities for children that will help them learn social skills such as sharing and good manners.

Clothing provider — Responsible for providing children with clothing that is comfortable, allows movement, and provides protection from the weather.

Caregiver — Responsible for providing constant care for children 24 hours a day.

Supporter — Enhances a positive self-esteem by helping children feel good about themselves. Provides support and love to children at all times. Provides support both when children achieve and when they fail. Enhances children's desire to try again.

Educational provider — Provides children with the best possible educational environment that matches their needs.

Guidance provider — Provides structure and guidelines while still allowing freedom within the structure.

Chauffeur — Responsible for transporting children to medical checkups, school, and various activities, such as birthday parties.

Safety guard — Provides a safe environment for the growth and development of children, and is constantly aware of possible dangers to children.

(Continued)

Empathizer   — Is able to understand why children feel the way they do. Is able to understand outbursts of anger and crying and can help children to deal with them.

Cleanliness supervisor — Responsible for keeping children clean and maintaining a clean environment.

Other qualifications:

_____ — _____

                                          _____

_____ — _____

                                          _____

_____ — _____

                                          _____

Parenting Job Description Profile

Job qualifications needed to meet the:

Physical needs of children

_____

_____

_____

_____

_____

_____

Intellectual needs of children

_____

_____

_____

_____

_____

_____

Social needs of children

_____

_____

_____

_____

_____

_____

Emotional needs of children

_____

_____

_____

_____

_____

_____

Which three qualifications listed above do you believe are the most important for a parent to possess? Explain why.

_____

_____

_____

_____

_____

Opinions About Parenting

Activity B

Chapter 1

Name _____

Date _____ Period _____

Read the following statements concerning parenting. Place a check in the column that best describes your opinion. Use the statements as discussion topics in class. (There are no right or wrong answers.)

Agree **Disagree** **Unsure**

_____ _____ _____ 1. Being a parent is the most rewarding source of fulfillment for a person.

_____ _____ _____ 2. Having children gives a person a special incentive to succeed in life.

_____ _____ _____ 3. Having children creates a stronger bond between husband and wife.

_____ _____ _____ 4. Deciding to begin parenting will greatly affect other aspects of an individual's life, such as educational and career goals.

_____ _____ _____ 5. For most people, parenting is a career choice over which they have little control.

_____ _____ _____ 6. Becoming a parent is a duty and an obligation.

_____ _____ _____ 7. Being a parent is only one of several important things a person can choose to be in life.

_____ _____ _____ 8. Most parents feel parenting has made their lives richer and it has been worth the effort.

_____ _____ _____ 9. Raising children can be more creative than most jobs.

_____ _____ _____ 10. Parenting can make a person more mature, responsible, and grown-up.

_____ _____ _____ 11. Parenting is more work than fun.

_____ _____ _____ 12. Parents should consider their own needs as well as their children's needs.

_____ _____ _____ 13. Raising children is boring and uncreative.

_____ _____ _____ 14. Having children causes a husband and wife to drift apart.

_____ _____ _____ 15. Being a parent can limit your career plans.

Choose a statement from the checklist above. Explain why you strongly agree or disagree with that statement.

I strongly (agree/disagree) with statement number _____ because _____

_____

_____

_____

_____

_____

Parenting Observation

Name _____

Date _____ Period _____

Spend 20 minutes silently observing how someone in a parenting role interacts with a child under the age of five. You may want to do your observation in a store or park. Following the observation, respond to the statements and questions below. Use your observation experience as a basis for class discussion.

Observation

Location: _____

Approximate age of child: _____ Approximate age of adult: _____

Observation notes: _____

_____

_____

_____

_____

_____

_____

1. Give your impression of the relationship between the child and the adult. _____

_____

_____

2. Did the child seem to enjoy being with the caregiver? _____

3. Did the caregiver seem to enjoy being with the child? _____

4. Describe the parenting techniques you observed. _____

_____

_____

_____

_____

_____

_____

5. Was the interaction between the child and the caregiver positive or negative? Explain. _____

_____

_____

_____

_____

_____

_____

Responsibilities and Rewards of Parenting

Activity D

Chapter 1

Name _____

Date _____ Period _____

This is a two-part activity. In the first part, you will survey three parents and ask them to respond to the questions below. You will then be asked to analyze the responses by writing a newspaper article. On the last page of the activity, you are asked to use your creativity to sketch or mount photos clipped from magazines to go with your article that depict some of the responsibilities and rewards of parenting.

Survey questions:

1. What do you feel are the major responsibilities of being a parent?

   Parent #1: _____

   _____

   Parent #2: _____

   _____

   Parent #3: _____

   _____

2. What do you feel are the major rewards of being a parent?

   Parent #1: _____

   _____

   Parent #2: _____

   _____

   Parent #3: _____

   _____

3. What changes occurred in your life when you became a parent?

   Parent #1: _____

   _____

   Parent #2: _____

   _____

   Parent #3: _____

   _____

4. What do you wish you had known before becoming a parent?

   Parent #1: _____

   _____

   Parent #2: _____

   _____

   Parent #3: _____

   _____

(Continued)

5. Do you feel you were ready to become a parent? Why or why not?

Parent #1: _____

_____

Parent #2: _____

_____

Parent #3: _____

_____

6. What other comments would you like to share regarding parenting?

Parent #1: _____

_____

Parent #2: _____

_____

Parent #3: _____

_____

In the space below, write a newspaper article in which you summarize your survey results by listing the responsibilities and rewards mentioned most often by the parents. Write a headline for your article.

_____

_____

_____

_____

_____

_____

_____

_____

_____

_____

_____

_____

_____

_____

_____

_____

_____

(Continued)

In the spaces below, sketch or mount photos that would illustrate the newspaper article you have written. Write a caption for each illustration.

_____   _____
_____   _____

_____   _____
_____   _____

2 Parenting: A Choice

The Personal Choice

Activity A

Chapter 2

Name _____

Date _____ Period _____

Ask yourself the following questions concerning your desire to be a parent. Indicate your responses below. (There are no right or wrong answers.)

Yes	No	
_____	_____	1. Would parenting affect my education and career?
_____	_____	2. If my career were fulfilling to me, would I want to take on the responsibility of parenting?
_____	_____	3. Would I be willing to give up the freedom of my social life to take on the responsibilities of caring for children?
_____	_____	4. Would I be able to combine going to school and raising children at the same time?
_____	_____	5. Have I developed a positive self-concept?
_____	_____	6. Can I supply the necessary financial support for raising children?
_____	_____	7. Would I like having my own children around all the time?
_____	_____	8. Do I enjoy working with children on their level, and would I be able to remain interested in the things they want to do?
_____	_____	9. Is it easy for me to talk to children?
_____	_____	10. Do I want to give children the love they need?
_____	_____	11. Am I patient enough to deal with the all-day and all-night responsibility of caring for children?
_____	_____	12. Would I be upset if my children needed time I had planned for myself?
_____	_____	13. Would I get angry and take this anger out on my children if I became upset over something they might have done?
_____	_____	14. Would I be able to help children learn right from wrong?
_____	_____	15. Would I be able to show love to a child under all circumstances?
_____	_____	16. When I spend time with children, am I calm and relaxed?
_____	_____	17. Do I consider having children as limiting and confining?
_____	_____	18. Do I like children?

Based on my answers to the questions above, if I had to decide today I would choose

_____ to become a parent _____ not to become a parent

List the reason for your response to the statement above. _____

_____

_____

Parenting Views

Name _____

Date _____ Period _____

Read the following statements. Indicate your views about parenting by checking the appropriate responses. Then use these statements as a basis for class discussion. (There are no right or wrong answers.)

Agree   Disagree   Unsure

_____ _____ _____ 1. I believe having a baby would enhance the love of a husband and wife and bring even more happiness to their lives.

_____ _____ _____ 2. I believe it is my duty to have children.

_____ _____ _____ 3. I believe if my spouse and I were having any problems in our marriage, having a child would solve them.

_____ _____ _____ 4. I believe having children helps a marriage stay strong and healthy.

_____ _____ _____ 5. I believe a husband and wife cannot find complete fulfillment of their love until they have a child.

_____ _____ _____ 6. I believe having children does not have to interfere with a career for either a husband or wife.

_____ _____ _____ 7. I believe children are expensive, but the joy they bring more than pays for the expense.

_____ _____ _____ 8. I believe having a baby may create a financial crisis.

_____ _____ _____ 9. I believe once a couple has children, they will automatically know how to be good parents.

_____ _____ _____ 10. I believe the primary relationship of a marriage should continue to be the husband-wife relationship, even following the birth of a child.

_____ _____ _____ 11. I believe the primary relationship of a marriage, once children are born, should be shifted to the parent-child relationship.

_____ _____ _____ 12. I believe having children will limit the marriage relationship and pose problems for the relationship.

_____ _____ _____ 13. I believe having children expands the marriage relationship and brings new experiences for the mother and father to share.

_____ _____ _____ 14. I believe if one spouse does not wish to be a parent, it would be better to remain childless regardless of the feelings of the other spouse.

_____ _____ _____ 15. I believe having children means shifts in time and commitments, and the husband-wife relationship will suffer.

_____ _____ _____ 16. Having children is the most important function of marriage.

_____ _____ _____ 17. A couple has a duty to have children to continue the family name.

_____ _____ _____ 18. It is important to have children so family traditions will continue.

I agree most strongly with statement #_____ because _____

_____

I disagree most strongly with statement #_____ because _____

_____

Your Feelings About Parenting

Activity C

Chapter 2

Name _____

Date _____ Period _____

Two groups of statements are given below. Check the reasons in each group that reveal your feelings about parenting. Space is provided to add reasons of your own. Then analyze your responses and write a brief summary paragraph. (There are no right or wrong answers.)

Reasons to have children:

_____ 1. Having a child is the ultimate expression of love between a husband and wife, and I would like to share this.

_____ 2. I would like to share my life with children.

_____ 3. Giving birth to a child is one of the greatest contributions a couple can make to the world.

_____ 4. Having children is one way my spouse and I can contribute to the future of the world.

_____ 5. I love children and want to include them in my life.

_____ 6. Having children would broaden and expand my life.

_____ 7. Having children is a special privilege.

_____ 8. Having children would make the loving relationship between my spouse and me even more secure.

_____ 9. I believe having children will make my marriage and career more meaningful.

_____ 10. I believe I can accept the responsibility of parenting.

_____ 11. I have such pleasant memories of my childhood that I would like to provide the same experiences for my children.

_____ 12. Having children is one of the most fulfilling goals I could have.

_____ 13. _____

_____ 14. _____

Reasons not to have children:

_____ 1. I like the freedom to come and go as I please.

_____ 2. I want to give my full attention to my career.

_____ 3. I want to devote my love and time to my spouse.

_____ 4. I enjoy being alone and spending time the way I choose.

_____ 5. I don't like children.

_____ 6. I think the world is too unsettled and crowded, and I would prefer not to bring any more children into the world.

_____ 7. I want to be financially secure, and having a child places a burden on that security.

_____ 8. I am an orderly person, and having children would create too many unexpected circumstances.

_____ 9. I don't think I would have the patience to deal with children.

_____ 10. I would resent having a child, and I would tend to feel as if I were "trapped" because of the child.

_____ 11. My childhood was unpleasant, and I would not want to have a child experience the same type of childhood.

(Continued)

_____ 12. I do not want the responsibility of parenting.

_____ 13. _____

_____ 14. _____

Analyze your responses:

Total of reasons you checked for having children: _____

Total of reasons you checked for not having children: _____

I feel the most important reason to have children is #_____ because _____

_____

_____

I feel the most important reason not to have children is #_____ because _____

_____

_____

Based upon my responses, I would probably choose (circle one)
    A. to become a parent
    B. not to become a parent
    C. not to decide right now, but to think about it

Summary: _____

_____

_____

_____

_____

_____

_____

_____

_____

_____

_____

_____

_____

_____

_____

_____

_____

_____

_____

_____

Your Time/Life Lines

Activity D   Name _____

Chapter 2   Date _____ Period _____

Think about your future. Make a list of the major goals you want to achieve in life. Then indicate on the time/life line when you plan to achieve these goals. Your goals may overlap in some time segments. Below the time/life line, summarize your goals in a brief paragraph. Then fill in the couple time/life line on the following page.

Individual time/life line:

Goals: 0   10   20   30   40   50   60   70   80   90

Summary: _____

_____

_____

_____

_____

_____

_____

_____

_____

_____

_____

_____

_____

_____

_____

_____

_____

_____

(Continued)

Now pretend you are married. Make a list of the major goals you and your spouse would want to achieve in life. Then indicate on the time/life line when you would expect to achieve these goals. Goals may overlap in some time segments. (You may wish to refer to the example of the time/life line in the text.) Below the time/life line, summarize the combined goals of you and your spouse in a brief paragraph.

Couple time line:

Goals:

	0	10	20	30	40	50	60	70	80	90
You										
Your Spouse										
You										
Your Spouse										
You										
Your Spouse										
You										
Your Spouse										
You										
Your Spouse										
You										
Your Spouse										
You										
Your Spouse										
You										
Your Spouse										
You										
Your Spouse										
You										
Your Spouse										

Summary: _____

_____

_____

_____

_____

_____

_____

_____

_____

_____

Characteristics of Parents

Name _____

Date _____ Period _____

Some characteristics used to describe personalities are listed below. List the characteristics you feel would be helpful to you if you become a parent and explain why.

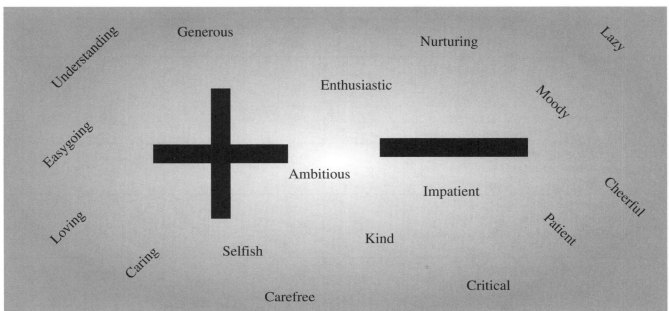

_____

_____

_____

_____

_____

_____

_____

_____

_____

_____

_____

_____

_____

_____

_____

_____

Couples and Children

Name _____

Date _____ Period _____

Read the following statements about couples and children. Indicate your feelings about parenting by responding to the following statements. Add four statements of your own. Discuss your responses in class. (There are no right or wrong answers.)

	Strongly Agree	Agree	Unsure	Disagree	Strongly Disagree
1. The decision about whether to have children should be made before a couple marry.					
2. Most married couples would be happier if they did not have any children.					
3. When a couple marry, the most ideal plan is to start a family as soon as possible.					
4. If a couple have differing opinions concerning whether to have children, it would be best to postpone starting a family.					
5. If a couple plan to get married but disagree about having children, it would be wise to reconsider the marriage plans.					
6. Having children makes a stronger bond between husband and wife.					
7. A man and woman who do not want children are being selfish.					
8. Having children complicates a marriage and causes many disagreements.					
9. Having children cements the bond between a husband and wife and tends to make a marriage stronger.					
10. Having children gives a couple the incentive to want to succeed in life.					
11.					
12.					
13.					
14.					

Costs of Having a Baby

Name _____

Date _____ Period _____

Research the costs of having a baby through the first week of life by finding out the following information. You may wish to consult recent parents, a hospital, a catalog, etc.

Costs of Having a Baby	
Medical costs (for mother and baby for an uncomplicated delivery)	
Baby's wardrobe	
Mother's maternity wardrobe	
Nursery furnishings	
Feeding equipment	
Bath items	
Car seat	
Baby carriage	
Diapers	
Miscellaneous	
	Total

Can you expect child-related expenses to increase as the child grows older? Explain.

_____

_____

_____

_____

_____

_____

_____

_____

_____

List ways parents can prepare for child-related expenses. _____

_____

_____

_____

_____

Children, Marriage, and Careers

Name _____

Date _____ Period _____

Read the following case studies. Then answer the following questions.

Case #1   Debbie and Renardo plan to get married. Renardo comes from a large family and looks forward to having several children. Debbie was an only child and is not really sure whether she wants children. They both have good jobs, and their financial future seems secure.

1. Are this couple's differences serious? Explain. _____

_____

_____

_____

_____

_____

_____

2. What could Debbie and Renardo do about their situation? _____

_____

_____

_____

_____

_____

_____

Case #2   Ann and Eric have been married for three years and want to have a child. Ann is an architect, and Eric is a lawyer. Ann and Eric both have high goals for their careers. They both plan to continue working after their child is born. They realize some problems may arise.

1. What type of problems might Ann and Eric face? _____

_____

_____

_____

_____

_____

2. What can Ann and Eric do to overcome these problems? _____

_____

_____

_____

_____

_____

Couple Profile

Name _____

Date _____ Period _____

Interview a mother and a father. Ask them to respond to the following questions. Compare the results of the interviews in class.

Approximate age of mother: _____

Approximate age of father: _____

Approximate age(s) of child or children: _____

1. When you said yes to parenting, to what other things did you say no?

   Mother: _____

   _____

   Father: _____

   _____

2. How did having a child affect your finances? _____

   _____

   _____

3. How will your child or children affect your finances in the future? _____

   _____

   _____

4. What were your expectations of your roles as parents?

   Mother: _____

   _____

   Father: _____

   _____

5. How did becoming a parent affect your career?

   Mother: _____

   _____

   Father: _____

   _____

6. What advice would you give to a couple considering becoming parents?

   Mother: _____

   _____

   _____

   Father: _____

   _____

   _____

Teen Parents: The Risks and Challenges

Activity J

Chapter 2

Name _____

Date _____ Period _____

Read about the following situations. Pretend you are a teen parent and describe how you would handle each situation. Compare and discuss your responses with other members of the class. Then answer the following questions.

1. You dreamed of a healthy baby. However, your baby was born prematurely. Many of the baby's organs are not fully developed. The doctor tells you the baby will suffer from long-term health problems. You do not have medical insurance. What should you do?

_____

_____

_____

_____

2. You are finding it difficult to cope with being a parent. You feel your baby is too demanding. It seems you have no time for yourself. What should you do?

_____

_____

_____

_____

3. You want to attend a rock concert. All your friends are going, and you haven't been out for weeks without your baby. You can't find a babysitter. What should you do?

_____

_____

_____

_____

4. Since you have become a parent, your family will have nothing to do with you. What should you do?

_____

_____

_____

_____

5. You find you have very little in common with your friends anymore. When they are talking about buying the latest CD, you are wondering about which baby formula to buy. When they are planning a trip to the mall, you are making an appointment with the pediatrician. You feel lonely and left out. What should you do?

_____

_____

_____

_____

(Continued)

6. You want to finish high school and perhaps go to college. You have no one to care for your baby while you are at school. Even if you could find someone, you probably couldn't afford the cost of child care. What should you do?

_____

_____

_____

_____

7. You want to find a high-paying job so you can support yourself and your baby. With your level of education, you are only qualified for low-paying jobs. What should you do?

_____

_____

_____

_____

8. You and your baby live with your parents. Although you are now a parent yourself, your parents still treat you like a child. What should you do?

_____

_____

_____

_____

9. For financial reasons, you, your spouse, and baby live with your parents. You appreciate the help your parents have given your family, but you and your spouse are beginning to resent their advice. You feel they are interfering with your marriage and parenting responsibilities. What should you do?

_____

_____

_____

_____

10. You thought having a baby would bring you and your spouse closer together. Instead you both feel trapped and you seem to be drifting apart. What should you do?

_____

_____

_____

_____

What do you think is the major challenge or risk teen parents must face?

_____

_____

_____

If you were a teen parent, how would you cope with this challenge or risk?

_____

_____

The Parenting Decision

Name _____

Date _____ Period _____

Pretend it is 10 years from now and you are married. You and your spouse are trying to decide about whether to become parents. Work through the six steps of the decision-making process as you make the decision.

Describe yourself 10 years from now. _____

_____

_____

_____

Describe your spouse. _____

_____

_____

_____

1. Identify the decision to be made.

   _____

   _____

2. List three possible alternatives.

   A. _____

   B. _____

   C. _____

3. Evaluate the consequences of each alternative.

   Alternative A: _____

   _____

   Alternative B: _____

   _____

   Alternative C: _____

   _____

4. Choose an alternative. Based on your evaluation of each alternative, which one would you choose?

   _____

5. Suppose you and your spouse have acted upon the decision. Describe what your life would be like based upon the decision you made.

   _____

   _____

   _____

6. Pretend it is 25 years from now. Do you feel you and your spouse made the right decision? _____ Explain why.

   _____

   _____

3 Families

How Families Are Formed

Activity A

Chapter 3

Name _____

Date _____ Period _____

Families can be formed in a variety of ways. Birth, marriage, and adoption are three ways families can be formed. Sometimes families are created through other circumstances. With each family structure shown below, give an example of how a family can be formed. Discuss your examples in class.

Parent Panel

Name _____

Date _____ Period _____

Invite parents who head different types of families to participate in a panel discussion about parenting. On a separate sheet of paper, prepare a list of questions to ask these parents. Then, in the space provided below, list what you believe are the pros and cons each family faces.

Married, Biological Parents

Pros (advantages, rewards): _____

_____

_____

_____

Cons (disadvantages, challenges): _____

_____

_____

_____

Single Parents

Pros (advantages, rewards): _____

_____

_____

_____

Cons (disadvantages, challenges): _____

_____

_____

_____

Parents in Stepfamilies

Pros (advantages, rewards): _____

_____

_____

_____

Cons (disadvantages, challenges): _____

_____

_____

_____

(Continued)

Adoptive Parents

Pros (advantages, rewards): _____

_____

_____

_____

Cons (disadvantages, challenges): _____

_____

_____

_____

Foster Parents

Pros (advantages, rewards): _____

_____

_____

_____

Cons (disadvantages, challenges): _____

_____

_____

_____

Parents in Extended Families

Pros (advantages, rewards): _____

_____

_____

_____

Cons (disadvantages, challenges): _____

_____

_____

_____

Family Structure Opinions

Activity C

Chapter 3

Name _____

Date _____ Period _____

Complete the checklist indicating your opinions about parents in various family structures. Choose one statement with which you strongly agree and one with which you strongly disagree and explain your reasoning. Discuss these statements in class.

Agree   Disagree

_____   _____   1. The nuclear family is able to fulfill the needs of children better than parents in other family structures.

_____   _____   2. A single parent can raise a child just as successfully as married parents can.

_____   _____   3. The nuclear family has the advantage of legal and social approval.

_____   _____   4. Children in a single-parent family can feel just as much love and security as children living with two parents.

_____   _____   5. A family headed by a well-adjusted single parent may be happier than a family headed by two parents who argue constantly.

_____   _____   6. A stepfamily will always be pulled in many different directions, but if the members of the family work together, they can have a happy family.

_____   _____   7. An extended family structure can allow extended family members to develop close relationships.

_____   _____   8. Couples without children are families just as couples with children are.

_____   _____   9. Grandparents play an active role in the lives of their grandchildren.

_____   _____   10. Family members can be happy and healthy in any family structure.

I strongly agree with statement _____ because _____

_____

_____

_____

_____

_____

_____

I strongly disagree with statement _____ because _____

_____

_____

_____

_____

_____

Family Structures

Name _____

Date _____ Period _____

The following family structures were described in the text: nuclear families, single-parent families, stepfamilies, extended families, and couples without children. Select one family structure and discuss its strengths. The explain why you think the family structure will become more or less common in the future.

_____

_____

_____

_____

_____

_____

_____

_____

_____

_____

_____

_____

_____

_____

_____

_____

_____

_____

_____

_____

_____

_____

_____

_____

_____

_____

_____

_____

_____

_____

Families: Yesterday, Today, and Tomorrow

Activity E

Chapter 3

Name _____

Date _____ Period _____

Invite a panel consisting of people of various generations, family therapists, and sociologists to discuss the following topics. Take notes during the discussion. Then write an article summarizing the key points and submit it to your school newspaper.

Panel members:

_____

_____

How are today's families like yesterday's families?

_____

_____

_____

How are today's families different from yesterday's families?

_____

_____

_____

How do you think the families of today will be like families in the future?

_____

_____

_____

How do you think families of today will be different from families in the future?

_____

_____

_____

What were the major challenges that faced families of yesterday?

_____

_____

_____

What are the major challenges facing families of today?

_____

_____

_____

What major challenges might families of tomorrow face?

_____

_____

_____

Your Family Roles

Name _____

Date_____ Period _____

Throughout your life, you will assume many roles and perform many functions as a member of a family. In the spaces provided, describe your present roles as a family member and then describe future roles you hope to assume and perform.

Your present roles as a family member:

_____

_____

_____

_____

_____

_____

_____

_____

_____

_____

_____

_____

_____

_____

_____

_____

_____

_____

_____

Your future roles as a family member:

_____

_____

_____

_____

_____

_____

_____

_____

Your Family Life Cycle

Name _____

Date _____ Period _____

The six stages in the family life cycle are described in your text. In the circle below, draw lines to indicate when you project you will begin and end each stage in your life cycle. Label each stage. (If you choose not to parent, your life cycle will include fewer stages.)

1. Which stage of your life cycle did you indicate would be the longest? _____

   Why?_____

   _____

   _____

   _____

2. Which stage of your life cycle did you project would be the shortest?

   Why?_____

   _____

   _____

   _____

(Continued)

3. Which stage do you feel will be the most enjoyable? _____

Why? _____

_____

_____

_____

4. Which stage do you feel will be the most difficult?

Why? _____

_____

_____

_____

5. Which stage do you think will require you to make the most adjustments? _____

Why? _____

_____

_____

_____

6. If parenting begins during the teen years, how would your life cycle be affected? _____

_____

_____

_____

7. Why might the beginning stage be longer for some couples? Discuss several reasons. _____

_____

_____

_____

_____

_____

How would this affect other stages of the life cycle? _____

_____

_____

_____

_____

8. What observations have you made as you have studied the family life cycle? _____

_____

_____

_____

_____

Grandparents

Name _____

Date _____ Period _____

Interview a grandparent. Find out the answers to the following questions.

1. How many grandchildren do you have?_____

2. What are their ages? _____

3. What roles do you play in the lives of your grandchildren? _____

_____

_____

_____

_____

_____

4. What are the challenges of being a grandparent? _____

_____

_____

_____

_____

_____

5. What are the rewards of being a grandparent?_____

_____

_____

_____

_____

_____

6. What are the advantages of being a grandparent? _____

_____

_____

_____

_____

_____

7. What are the disadvantages of being a grandparent?_____

_____

_____

_____

_____

_____

A Unique Family

Name _____

Date _____ Period _____

Describe a family in terms of what makes it unique. Describe the family in terms of the factors given below. (The family you choose may be your own family or any other family of your choice.) Compare your responses with those of others in the class. Then answer the following questions.

Describe the family.

_____

_____

_____

_____

_____

Describe the ethnic and cultural background of the family.

_____

_____

_____

_____

_____

Describe the lifestyle of the family.

_____

_____

_____

_____

_____

Describe the community in which the family lives.

_____

_____

_____

_____

_____

(Continued)

Describe how the media influences the family.

_____

_____

_____

_____

_____

_____

Describe how technology influences the family.

_____

_____

_____

_____

_____

_____

Are any two families exactly alike? Explain.

_____

_____

_____

_____

_____

_____

_____

_____

_____

_____

_____

_____

_____

_____

_____

_____

_____

_____

4 Effective Parenting

Types of Development

Activity A

Chapter 4

Name _____

Date _____ Period _____

It is important for parents to know how children develop. Define each of the following types of development. Then list at least four examples of each type of development.

Physical development: _____

_____

_____

Examples: _____

_____

_____

_____

Intellectual development: _____

_____

Examples: _____

_____

_____

_____

Emotional development: _____

_____

Examples: _____

_____

_____

_____

Social development: _____

_____

Examples: _____

_____

_____

_____

Patterns of Development

Activity B

Chapter 4

Name _____

Date _____ Period _____

Fill in the blanks in the following paragraph with words related to patterns of development.

One basic pattern of development is that development proceeds, in general, from ___(1)___ to foot. Another basic pattern of development proceeds, in general, from the ___(2)___ of the body outward. A baby's first learned movement is to ___(3)___. Later, the baby learns to control the ___(4)___ of the arms and legs. Still later, a baby gains control of the ___(5)___. Development follows many predictable ___(6)___. Children ___(7)___ before they stand, stand before they ___(8)___, and walk before they ___(9)___. When learning to talk, children first learn to make ___(10)___. Gradually, they build upon that skill and learn to say ___(11)___. As development continues, children learn to put words together in ___(12)___.

1. _____

2. _____

3. _____

4. _____

5. _____

6. _____

7. _____

8. _____

9. _____

10. _____

11. _____

12. _____

Each child is a unique individual from the moment of birth. Explain what this should mean to parents.

_____

_____

_____

_____

_____

_____

_____

_____

_____

_____

_____

_____

_____

_____

_____

_____

Heredity or Environment?

Activity C

Name _____

Chapter 4

Date _____ Period _____

Each child is unique based on his or her heredity and environment. In the space provided, define *heredity* and *environment*. Then look at the list below and distinguish between items that can be linked to heredity and those that can be linked to environment. If the item is due to heredity, write an **H** in the blank. If the item is due to environment, write an **E** in the blank. (Some of these items may be a combination of heredity and environment.)

Heredity: _____

_____

_____

Environment: _____

_____

_____

_____ 1. Michael has green eyes.

_____ 2. Rachel has a lot of self-confidence.

_____ 3. Vincent is tall like his mother.

_____ 4. Brant lives in a nice house.

_____ 5. Shalonda has dark skin.

_____ 6. Catina lives with her grandparents.

_____ 7. Julia visits the library often.

_____ 8. Kayla plays the piano quite well.

_____ 9. Patrice lives in a small apartment.

_____ 10. Albert is shy around strangers.

_____ 11. Bill and his brother Ben look alike.

_____ 12. Marcel often scores high on tests in school.

_____ 13. Carly has red hair.

_____ 14. Jordan has many friends.

_____ 15. Jarret has a great sense of humor.

Needs of Children and Parents

Name _____

Date _____ Period _____

Think about the needs of children and parents listed below. Give an example of how each of the needs can be met.

Need	Example
1. Children need structure in their lives to develop a sense of order and purpose.	
2. Children need to recognize the consequences of their actions.	
3. Children need a variety of experiences to develop well-rounded personalities.	
4. Children need to have enriching conversations with adults.	
5. Parents need to develop a sense of what is important in their lives.	
6. Parents need to maintain realistic expectations and reasonable discipline.	
7. Parents need to recognize each child as an individual.	
8. Parents need to recognize the power of communication.	

Balancing Needs of Parents and Their Children

Activity E

Chapter 4

Name _____

Date _____ Period _____

It is difficult to strike a balance between parents' needs and their children's needs. On the scale below, list some needs of parents and some needs of children. Then answer the following questions.

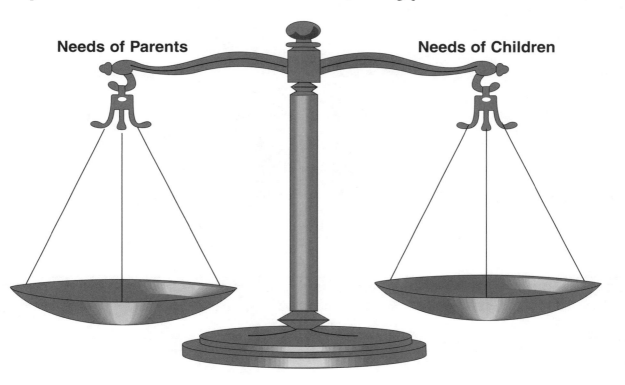

Needs of Parents   **Needs of Children**

1. Describe how you, as a parent, would try to balance these needs. _____

_____

_____

_____

_____

_____

_____

_____

_____

2. Do parents help their children or hinder them when they let children know they, as parents, have needs that need to be fulfilled? Explain. _____

_____

_____

_____

_____

Characteristics of Strong Families

Activity F

Chapter 4

Name _____

Date _____ Period _____

The family serves as a foundation on which children build their own independent lives. On each of the "bricks" in the foundation below, write what you believe are characteristics of strong families. Compare your foundations with those of others in class.

Communication Enhancers and Inhibitors

Activity G

Chapter 4

Name _____

Date _____ Period _____

Read each of the following statements. If a statement describes a situation that enhances communication, write an **E** in the blank. If a statement describes a situation that inhibits communication, write an **I** in the blank.

_____ 1. When speaking to his children, Greg uses a gruff tone of voice.

_____ 2. Members of the Perez family are encouraged to express good feelings as well as bad feelings.

_____ 3. Ann always tells her daughter, Robin, what to do.

_____ 4. Whenever Aaron has a problem with his friends or teachers, his mother always tries to solve it for him.

_____ 5. Carol uses "I" messages to communicate with members of her family.

_____ 6. The Washington family communicates using "we" messages.

_____ 7. Joe always makes light of his daughter Ellen's problems by telling her not to worry about them.

_____ 8. Members of the Smith family tend to keep their feelings to themselves.

_____ 9. Tasha knows she can go to her parents to discuss any problem.

_____ 10. Jill blames her mom for all her problems.

_____ 11. Rosa constantly interrupts when her mother talks to her.

_____ 12. Matt assumes his mom won't understand his problems.

_____ 13. When Rachel and her sister Lindsay have an argument, their mother does not interfere and allows them to handle the problem themselves.

_____ 14. Larry demands that his children follow his orders with no discussion.

_____ 15. Sam uses active listening when communicating with his family.

_____ 16. Latonia avoids jumping to conclusions until she listens to her son's explanation of why he arrived home late.

_____ 17. Elena lets her children know she is always interested and concerned about them.

_____ 18. Sabrina approaches her dad with problems as soon as he arrives home from a trying day at the office.

_____ 19. Mary believes it is her duty as a parent to preach to her children about how she wants them to behave.

_____ 20. Tawanda uses "you" messages to communicate with members of her family.

Building a Child's Self-Concept and Self-Esteem

Parents play a vital role in building their children's self-concept and self-esteem. In the space provided, give examples of how parents can help their children build positive self-concepts and self-esteems.

Parent Helpers

Activity I

Chapter 4

Name _____

Date _____ Period _____

Interview someone from a local support group or agency that helps parents. Find out the information below. Share this information with members of your class. (This information can be compiled to produce a local directory of parent support groups and agencies.)

Name of support group or agency: _____

Contact person: _____

Address: _____

Telephone: _____

Hours: _____

Sponsorship (such as government agency, church, private group): _____

_____

Types of situations with which this support group or agency deals: _____

_____

_____

_____

_____

_____

_____

How this support group or agency can help: _____

_____

_____

_____

_____

_____

_____

_____

_____

_____

_____

Building a Parent Support System

Name _____

Date _____ Period _____

Pretend you are a parent. Describe how each of the following might help you by becoming a part of your parent support system.

	Types of Situations	How They Could Help
Your family		
Friends		
Neighbors		
Teachers		
Colleagues		
Religious organizations		
Agencies		
Support groups		

5 Planning a Family

Planning Considerations

Activity A

Chapter 5

Name _____

Date _____ Period _____

Read the following case studies. Working in a small group, respond to the statements below. Compare your group's responses to those of other groups.

Case #1   *Carlos and Rita are both 23 years old. They have been married for six months and have found marriage to be more of an adjustment than they had thought it would be. They both have good jobs and enjoy their hobbies of travel and skiing. They both want children, but they are not sure when. They do know they want to be financially secure before they have a child because Rita plans to quit her job when they have a child.*

1. Carlos and Rita should probably: (Circle one.)

   A. start having children as soon as possible

   B. postpone parenthood for a while

   Explain your answer. _____

_____

_____

_____

_____

_____

_____

_____

_____

2. List factors Carlos and Rita should consider before becoming parents. Explain why these factors should be considered.

_____

_____

_____

_____

_____

_____

_____

_____

_____

_____

(Continued)

Case #2   *Ellen and Michael have been married for three years and have one child, Daniel, who is six months old. Daniel is a healthy baby, and Ellen and Michael really enjoy being parents. They are trying to decide if and when to have other children.*

Explain how the following factors should influence Ellen and Michael's decision.

1. Emotional factors:_____

_____

_____

_____

_____

2. Financial factors: _____

_____

_____

_____

_____

3. The spacing of children:

The likely effects on Daniel: _____

_____

_____

_____

_____

The likely effects on Ellen's health: _____

_____

_____

_____

_____

Future educational costs: _____

_____

_____

_____

_____

Factors to Consider

Name _____

Date _____ Period _____

Factors a couple should consider before having children are listed below. Next to each factor, explain how it might affect a couple's decision to have a child. Circle the number of the factor you consider most important. Discuss the reasons for your choice in class.

1. The security of the marriage relationship: _____

_____

_____

_____

2. The emotional maturity of the couple: _____

_____

_____

_____

3. The health of the husband and wife: _____

_____

_____

_____

4. The age of the couple, particularly that of the wife: _____

_____

_____

_____

5. The personal and mutual goals of the husband and wife: _____

_____

_____

_____

6. The financial security of the couple: _____

_____

_____

_____

7. Other factors: _____

_____

_____

_____

Human Reproduction

Match the following terms with their descriptive phrases.

Male

_____ 1. The urethra extends through this organ.

_____ 2. Sperm are stored and later carried through this long, narrow tube up into the man's pelvic cavity.

_____ 3. Contains the male set of 23 chromosomes.

_____ 4. A coiled tube where the sperm mature.

_____ 5. Where sperm are produced.

_____ 6. Duct that extends through the penis and through which sperm leave the body.

_____ 7. Secretions from three sets of glands and the sperm.

A. sperm
B. testes
C. epididymis
D. vas deferens
E. urethra
F. penis
G. semen

Female

_____ 8. Where eggs are stored.

_____ 9. Where sperm are deposited.

_____ 10. The process by which an egg is released from the ovaries.

_____ 11. Where fertilization of the egg by the sperm takes place.

_____ 12. Contains the female set of 23 chromosomes.

_____ 13. The inner lining of the uterus.

_____ 14. A hollow, muscular organ that holds and nourishes a fertilized egg as it develops into a baby.

A. egg
B. ovaries
C. ovulation
D. fallopian tube
E. vagina
F. uterus
G. endometrium

Family Planning Opinions

Activity D

Chapter 5

Name _____

Date _____ Period _____

Indicate your opinion about the following statements. Use these statements as a basis for class discussion. (There are no right or wrong answers.) Then complete the statements below.

Agree	Disagree	Unsure	
_____	_____	_____	1. Planning a family means parenthood is by choice rather than by chance.
_____	_____	_____	2. A couple really cannot discuss and choose family planning until they are actually married.
_____	_____	_____	3. The best time for a couple to discuss family planning is before marriage.
_____	_____	_____	4. It is important that a couple mutually agree on family planning.
_____	_____	_____	5. Having a baby early in marriage will help the bonding process between a new husband and wife.
_____	_____	_____	6. A couple should have at least 18 months to learn their roles as husband and wife before they start planning new roles as mother and father.
_____	_____	_____	7. If either husband or wife have other major life goals, it is best if they delay parenthood.
_____	_____	_____	8. By delaying parenthood until they have reached total financial security, a couple may find they will never be ready for parenthood.
_____	_____	_____	9. An important factor to consider in the spacing of several children is future educational costs.
_____	_____	_____	10. Children should be spaced three to four years apart.
_____	_____	_____	11. Children should be about a year apart in age.
_____	_____	_____	12. Every child has the right to be wanted.
_____	_____	_____	13. Family planning decisions must be based on religious, family, and personal beliefs.

I agree most strongly with statement #_____ because _____

_____

_____

_____

_____

I disagree most strongly with statement #_____ because _____

_____

_____

_____

_____

Options for Infertile Couples

Activity E

Chapter 5

Name _____

Date _____ Period _____

Pretend you and your spouse are infertile. Choose one of the options for infertile couples that was described in the text. Using current periodicals and/or Internet sources, research current developments regarding the option you have chosen. Then describe what you feel are the advantages and disadvantages of that option.

Option: _____

Current developments: _____

_____

_____

_____

_____

_____

_____

_____

_____

_____

_____

_____

_____

Advantages: _____

_____

_____

_____

_____

_____

Disadvantages: _____

_____

_____

_____

_____

_____

6 Pregnancy

Month-by-Month Development

Activity A

Chapter 6

Name _____

Date _____ Period _____

The months of prenatal development are listed below. In the space provided, briefly describe the prenatal development that occurs during each month.

End of first month: _____

_____

_____

_____

_____

End of second month: _____

_____

_____

_____

_____

End of third month: _____

_____

_____

_____

_____

End of fourth month: _____

_____

_____

_____

_____

(Continued)

End of fifth month: _____
_____
_____
_____
_____
_____

End of sixth month: _____
_____
_____
_____
_____
_____

End of seventh month: _____
_____
_____
_____
_____
_____

End of eighth month: _____
_____
_____
_____
_____
_____

End of ninth month: _____
_____
_____
_____
_____
_____

Pregnancy Changes

Activity B

Chapter 6

Name _____

Date _____ Period _____

Look at the diagram below. Identify each of the parts as indicated. Then give a brief description of each.

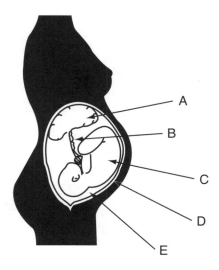

A. _____ : _____

_____

_____

_____

B. _____ : _____

_____

_____

_____

C. _____ : _____

_____

_____

_____

D. _____ : _____

_____

_____

_____

E. _____ : _____

_____

_____

_____

Pregnancy Terms

Name _____

Date _____ Period _____

Unscramble the letters below to reveal terms associated with pregnancy. Then define each term.

1. RTITSMERE __ __ __ __ __ __ __ __ __

_____

_____

2. NPICCTOONE __ __ __ __ __ __ __ __ __ __

_____

_____

3. GTZOEY __ __ __ __ __ __

_____

_____

4. NAALTRPE VMEEEPDNLTO __ __ __ __ __ __ __ __   __ __ __ __ __ __ __ __ __ __

_____

_____

5. YBTTSSOCAL __ __ __ __ __ __ __ __ __ __

_____

_____

6. NTLEAAPC __ __ __ __ __ __ __ __

_____

_____

7. LMLAUIIBC RDOC __ __ __ __ __ __ __ __   __ __ __ __

_____

_____

8. TINIACMO DLIFU __ __ __ __ __ __ __ __   __ __ __ __ __

_____

_____

9. YRMEOB __ __ __ __ __ __

_____

_____

10. TSUFE __ __ __ __ __

_____

_____

Complications During Pregnancy

Activity D

Chapter 6

Name _____

Date _____ Period _____

Causes of complications that sometimes occur during pregnancy are listed below. Briefly describe the possible effects of these complications on the mother and the baby.

Cause of Complications	Possible Effects on the Mother	Possible Effects on the Baby
Pregnancy-Induced hypertension (PIH)		
Rubella		
Rh factor disorder		
Gonorrhea		

Name _____

Cause of Complications	Possible Effects on the Mother	Possible Effects on the Baby
Syphilis		
Herpes		
Chlamydia		
HIV/AIDS		

7 Prenatal Care

Ask the Doctor

Activity A

Chapter 7

Name _____

Date _____ Period _____

Pretend you are pregnant or you think you are pregnant. Prepare a list of 10 questions you would ask a doctor on your first visit. Then ask a doctor to speak to the class and find out the answers to the questions.

1. _____

_____

_____

2. _____

_____

_____

3. _____

_____

_____

4. _____

_____

_____

5. _____

_____

_____

6. _____

_____

_____

7. _____

_____

_____

8. _____

_____

_____

9. _____

_____

_____

10. _____

_____

_____

Diet During Pregnancy

Name _____

Date _____ Period _____

Plan a week's diet for a pregnant woman. Use the chart in 7-9 of the text as a guideline.

	Breakfast	Lunch	Dinner	Snacks
Monday				
Tuesday				
Wednesday				
Thursday				
Friday				
Saturday				
Sunday				

Pregnancy Considerations

Activity C   Name _____

Chapter 7   Date _____ Period _____

Read the following cases. Respond to the following questions.

Case #1   Shyrell is pregnant. The first day of her last normal menstrual period was January 3.

What will be the approximate birth date of Shyrell's baby? _____

_____

Case #2   Julie has been taking an aerobics class for several years. Now that she is pregnant, she wonders whether it is a good idea to continue taking the class.

What should Julie do?_____

_____

_____

_____

_____

_____

_____

Case #3   Sue and Dan are expecting a baby. They both smoke heavily. Sue's doctor told her to quit, at least during pregnancy. Sue tries to quit, but when Dan smokes, she joins him.

What risks are Sue and Dan taking?_____

_____

_____

_____

_____

_____

_____

Case #4   Leavella is a teenager. She is also pregnant. Before Leavella became pregnant, she would eat junk foods one week and then try a fad diet the next week. Leavella's doctor has now put her on a strict nutritional program.

Why has her doctor done this? _____

_____

_____

_____

_____

_____

Deadly Consequences

Name _____

Date _____ Period _____

Factors that increase health risks to both the mother and baby are listed in the chart below. In the column on the right, list the consequences of each factor.

Factors That Increase Health Risks	Consequences
Medications and over-the-counter drugs	
Illegal drugs	
Alcohol	
Smoking	
Caffeine	
X rays	

8 Decisions Facing Parents-to-Be

Childbirth Preparation Class Observation

Activity A

Chapter 8

Name _____

Date _____ Period _____

Obtain permission to visit a childbirth preparation class. Based upon your observation, answer the questions below.

Location of childbirth preparation class: _____

1. What was the topic of the childbirth preparation class you attended?

   _____

2. What types of questions did the parents-to-be ask?

   _____

   _____

   _____

   _____

3. How would this class help the parents-to-be prepare for the birth of their baby?

   _____

   _____

   _____

   _____

4. What suggestions were given to help couples learn how to actively participate in their baby's birth?

   _____

   _____

   _____

   _____

   _____

5. If you were a parent-to-be, why would or wouldn't you participate in a childbirth preparation class?

   _____

   _____

   _____

   _____

Birthplace Options

Name _____

Date _____ Period _____

Arrange to tour at least two of the following birthplace options and respond to the following statements.

Option **A**: Traditional hospital delivery room

Option **B**: Hospital birthing room

Option **C**: Birth center

I visited Option _____ and Option _____.

Description of Option _____:

_____

_____

Description of Option _____:

_____

_____

Advantages of Option _____:

_____

_____

Disadvantages of Option _____:

_____

_____

Advantages of Option _____:

_____

_____

Disadvantages of Option _____:

_____

_____

If I were a parent-to-be, I would choose Option _____ because:

_____

_____

_____

If I were a parent-to-be, I would not choose Option _____ because:

_____

_____

_____

Types of Diapers

Name _____

Date _____ Period _____

Compare various types of diapers by completing the chart below.

Type	Cost (per package or order)	Cost (each)	Characteristics (comfort, convenience, etc.)
Cloth (brands):			
Diaper services:			
Disposable (brands):			

If I were a parent, the type of diaper(s) I would use for my baby would be _____ because

_____

_____

_____

_____

_____

_____

The Newborn's Wardrobe

Activity D

Chapter 8

Name _____

Date _____ Period _____

Items needed by the newborn are listed below. Refer to the wardrobe chart in Chapter 8 of the text to determine the quantity of each item needed. Then use catalogs, newspaper advertisements, or information obtained from a local store to determine the costs of the various items. Compare your costs with those of other class members.

Item	Quantity Needed	Cost Per Item	Total Cost Per Item
Diapers			
Diaper liners			
Diaper pins			
Vinyl pants			
Cotton knit shirts			
Cotton knit nightgowns			
Stretch garments			
Special outfits			
Sweaters			
Caps or hats			
Mittens and booties			
Blanket sleeper or bunting			
Cotton receiving blankets			
Acrylic or wool blankets			
		Total	

What should be the most important consideration when shopping for clothes for a newborn? Explain why.

_____

_____

_____

_____

_____

_____

_____

_____

_____

_____

_____

_____

_____

Breast- or Formula-Feeding

Activity E

Chapter 8

Name _____

Date _____ Period _____

Visit the library. Research current articles about breast-feeding and formula-feeding. Read three articles. Summarize them in the space below. Then complete the following statement.

Source:_____

Summary: _____

_____

_____

_____

_____

_____

_____

Source:_____

Summary: _____

_____

_____

_____

_____

_____

_____

Source:_____

Summary: _____

_____

_____

_____

_____

_____

_____

If I were a parent, I would choose _____-feeding for my baby because _____

_____

_____

_____

_____

Parental Employment

Survey parents who are both employed about how they balance their family life and work. Compare and share your results with members of the class.

1. Describe the stress involved in trying to balance your multiple roles of employee, parent, spouse, and homemaker.

_____

_____

2. Describe your company's parental leave policy.

_____

_____

3. Describe your child care arrangements.

_____

_____

4. Describe the division of labor regarding household tasks.

_____

_____

5. What is most challenging about combining a family and career?

_____

_____

6. How does your family affect your work?

_____

_____

7. How does your work affect your family?

_____

_____

8. What do you consider to be the advantages of having children and working?

_____

_____

9. What do you consider to be the disadvantages of having children and working?

_____

_____

10. What strategies have you found helpful in achieving your mutual goals?

_____

_____

9 Childbirth

Signs and Stages of Labor

Activity A

Chapter 9

Name _____

Date _____ Period _____

Complete the following exercise about the signs and stages of labor.

A woman may notice several signs labor is approaching. List three signs that might indicate labor will soon occur.

1. _____

2. _____

3. _____

Various events that occur during labor are listed below. Complete the chart on the next page concerning the stages of labor. Under the "Events That Occur" column, list the numbers from the list below that occur during the various stages of labor.

Events that occur during labor:

1. Contractions continue and cause the placenta to separate from the wall of the uterus.

2. Uterine contractions begin.

3. The cervix dilates.

4. Crowning occurs.

5. An episiotomy is performed.

6. The doctor gently turns the baby's head so the shoulders can slide out easily.

7. The amnio-chorionic membrane ruptures.

8. Amniotic fluid is suctioned from the baby's nose and mouth.

9. The placenta is examined to make sure it has not torn and left excess tissue in the uterus.

10. The umbilical cord is cut.

(Continued)

Stages of Labor

	Known as:	Begins When:	Ends When:	Average Length of Time:	Events That Occur:
First stage					
Second stage					
Third stage					

Hospital Procedures

Name _____

Date _____ Period _____

Visit or call a local hospital. Inquire about the hospital's procedures regarding childbirth by asking the following questions. You may also ask any questions of your own.

1. To speed up the admittance process, are patients allowed to fill out admittance forms several weeks before the delivery date?

_____

2. What happens when the expectant parents arrive at the hospital during labor?

_____

_____

_____

_____

_____

_____

3. What procedures are followed during labor?

_____

_____

_____

_____

_____

_____

4. What procedures are followed during a typical delivery?

_____

_____

_____

_____

_____

_____

5. What procedures are followed for a cesarean delivery?

_____

_____

_____

_____

_____

_____

(Continued)

6. What procedures are followed for a premature delivery?

_____

_____

_____

_____

_____

_____

7. What procedures are followed during recovery?

_____

_____

_____

_____

_____

_____

8. Does the baby stay in the mother's room or in the nursery?

_____

_____

_____

_____

_____

_____

9. Who may and may not visit? What are visiting hours?

_____

_____

10. Other procedures or additional questions:

_____

_____

_____

_____

_____

Pretend you are an expectant parent. Based on the information you have gathered, would you want to experience childbirth at this hospital? Why or why not?

_____

_____

_____

_____

Methods of Childbirth

Name _____

Date _____ Period _____

Research the methods of childbirth available in your area. Report your findings to the class. (The class may be divided into four groups. Then each student may record information from each group as reports are given.)

Traditional Childbirth:

An area hospital providing this method:_____

Costs involved:

    Delivery costs: _____

    Hospital room costs:_____

    Nursery costs: _____

Procedure for admittance: _____

_____

_____

_____

Procedures during labor and delivery:

    For mother: _____

    _____

    _____

    For baby:_____

    _____

    _____

    For father (or other family members, etc.): _____

    _____

    _____

Procedures after delivery: _____

_____

_____

_____

Length of hospital stay:_____

Educational assistance provided (bathing baby, feeding baby, etc.)_____

_____

_____

_____

_____

(Continued)

Family-Centered Childbirth:

An area hospital providing this method:_____

Costs involved:

    Delivery costs: _____

    Hospital room costs: _____

    Nursery costs: _____

Procedure for admittance: _____

_____

_____

_____

Procedures during labor and delivery:

    For mother: _____

    _____

    _____

    For baby:_____

    _____

    _____

    For father (or other family members, etc.): _____

    _____

    _____

Procedures after delivery: _____

_____

_____

_____

Length of hospital stay:_____

Educational assistance provided (bathing baby, feeding baby, etc.)_____

_____

_____

_____

_____

(Continued)

Name _____

Lamaze Method:

An area hospital providing this method:_____

Costs involved:

    Delivery costs: _____

    Hospital room costs:_____

    Nursery costs:_____

Procedure for admittance: _____

_____

_____

_____

Procedures during labor and delivery:

    For mother: _____

_____

_____

    For baby:_____

_____

_____

    For father (or other family members, etc.): _____

_____

_____

Procedures after delivery: _____

_____

_____

_____

Length of hospital stay:_____

Educational assistance provided (bathing baby, feeding baby, etc.)_____

_____

_____

_____

_____

(Continued)

Leboyer Method:

An area hospital providing this method:_____

Costs involved:

    Delivery costs: _____

    Hospital room costs: _____

    Nursery costs: _____

Procedure for admittance: _____

_____

_____

_____

Procedures during labor and delivery:

    For mother: _____

    _____

    _____

    For baby:_____

    _____

    _____

    For father (or other family members, etc.): _____

    _____

    _____

Procedures after delivery: _____

_____

_____

_____

Length of hospital stay:_____

Educational assistance provided (bathing baby, feeding baby, etc.)_____

_____

_____

_____

_____

(Continued)

Cesarean Delivery:

An area hospital providing this method:_____

Costs involved:

    Delivery costs: _____

    Hospital room costs:_____

    Nursery costs: _____

Procedure for admittance: _____

_____

_____

_____

Procedures during labor and delivery:

    For mother: _____

    _____

    _____

    For baby:_____

    _____

    _____

    For father (or other family members, etc.): _____

    _____

    _____

Procedures after delivery: _____

_____

_____

_____

Length of hospital stay:_____

Educational assistance provided (bathing baby, feeding baby, etc.)_____

_____

_____

_____

_____

Childbirth Crossword

(Continued)

Across

1. _____-centered childbirth is based on the belief that childbirth affects the family as a unit as well as each family member as an individual.

5. The _____ stage of labor begins when the cervix is fully dilated.

6. In the _____ method of childbirth, parents-to-be prepare themselves for the experience of childbirth.

8. A depression mothers may feel shortly after childbirth is "the baby _____."

10. An _____ is a small cut at the opening of the birth canal that allows more room for the baby to be born.

12. _____ refers to the moment the baby's head is first seen.

15. In _____ childbirth, attention is focused on the woman's and baby's health and on the woman's comfort.

16. The _____ period is that period of time following the delivery of the baby.

Down

2. The _____ text is used to evaluate the overall physical condition of newborns.

3. _____ is a series of changes in the mother's body that enables the baby to be born.

4. _____ occurs as the head of the fetus descends down into the mother's pelvis.

6. The _____ method of childbirth focuses on the birth experience of the baby.

7. Contractions are _____ felt during labor when the muscles of the uterus tense.

9. An operation in which a baby is delivered through incisions in the abdomen and uterus is called a _____ delivery.

11. The first stage of labor is the _____ stage.

13. During the _____ stage of labor, the placenta is delivered.

14. _____ is the formation of close emotional ties between parents and child.

Childbirth Choices

Pretend you are about to become a parent. Respond to the statement and questions below.

1. Describe the childbirth method you would prefer. _____

_____

_____

_____

_____

_____

2. What would be the pros of this method? _____

_____

_____

_____

_____

_____

3. What would be the cons of this method? _____

_____

_____

_____

_____

_____

4. What alternate method would you choose? Explain why. _____

_____

_____

_____

_____

5. Which method would you definitely *not* choose? Explain why. _____

_____

_____

_____

_____

_____

Childbirth Case Studies

Name _____

Date _____ Period _____

Read the following case studies. Respond to the questions below.

Case #1   *Joyce is in her last month of pregnancy. She is packing a bag with the items she and her baby will need while in the hospital.*

What should Joyce pack for herself and for her baby?

Mother's needs: _____

_____

_____

_____

_____

_____

_____

Baby's needs: _____

_____

_____

_____

_____

_____

_____

Case #2   *Tetra and Guy are expecting their first baby. They are very much interested in being prepared for childbirth. They feel the more they know about what to expect, the more they will enjoy the experience. Guy wants to be with Tetra throughout labor and delivery and witness the birth of their child.*

Which method of childbirth would probably be best for Tetra and Guy? Explain why.

_____

_____

_____

_____

_____

_____

_____

_____

_____

(Continued)

Case #3   *Maria and Mark are expecting their third child. Their children Paul and Noel, ages seven and nine, have expressed interest in facts about pregnancy and childbirth. Maria and Mark want their entire family to be involved in the birth of the baby.*

Which childbirth method would probably be best for their family? Explain why. _____

_____

_____

_____

_____

_____

_____

_____

_____

_____

_____

_____

Case #4   *Judy and Mike had a baby several weeks ago. They are thrilled about the birth of their baby. Since Judy and the baby have been home, there has been a steady stream of visitors. Judy and Mike have not only been busy taking care of the baby, but also cleaning house and entertaining their visitors. Lately, they have been feeling depressed. They don't understand why they feel this way since they are happy about the birth of their baby.*

What is the name for this depression? _____

_____

What should Judy and Mike do?_____

_____

_____

_____

_____

_____

_____

_____

_____

_____

_____

10 New Parents, New Baby

New Parents

Activity A

Chapter 10

Name _____

Date _____ Period _____

Interview new parents or ask new parents to come to class to relate experiences they had when they first became parents. Find out the answers to the following questions.

1. What feelings did you experience when you were first told you had a new son or daughter?

Mother: _____

_____

_____

_____

Father: _____

_____

_____

_____

2. Did your feelings toward your spouse change after the birth of your baby? Explain.

Mother: _____

_____

_____

_____

Father: _____

_____

_____

_____

3. How did the birth of your baby affect your schedule?

Mother: _____

_____

_____

_____

Father: _____

_____

_____

_____

(Continued)

4. How has your baby affected your freedom to come and go as you please?

Mother: _____

_____

_____

_____

Father: _____

_____

_____

_____

5. What are some of the worries you had concerning your new baby?

Mother: _____

_____

_____

_____

Father: _____

_____

_____

_____

6. What advice would you give to new parents when they first bring their baby home?

Mother: _____

_____

_____

_____

Father: _____

_____

_____

_____

Additional notes and questions:

_____

_____

_____

_____

_____

_____

How Newborns Look

Name _____

Date _____ Period _____

Write phrases describing how newborns look at birth by filling in the blanks below. Then complete the following sentence.

hair _____   chest_____   body proportions _____

_____   _____   _____

nose_____   shoulders _____   skin_____

_____   _____   _____

shape of head _____

abdomen_____

ears _____   _____

_____   fingers _____

eyebrows_____   _____

_____   legs_____

eyelashes_____   _____

_____

cheeks _____   average weight_____

_____   _____

chin _____   average length _____

_____   _____

neck_____

_____

Complete this sentence and then explain your reasoning.

What impresses me most about newborns is _____

_____

_____

_____

_____

_____

_____

_____

_____

_____

_____

_____

_____

Senses of the Newborn

Name _____

Date_____ Period _____

Fill in the blanks in the following paragraphs with words that describe the senses of newborns.

Sense of Sight:

The newborn's eyes function from the moment of _____. Both eyes don't always work together right away because the _____ are not well developed. The newborn's eyes are sensitive to _____. The newborn's eyes _____ best at a distance of 8 to 12 inches. When looking at things, they prefer moving objects to _____ ones. By the age of three weeks, the _____ _____ is what newborns like most to see.

Sense of Hearing:

The ability to _____ develops even before birth. Newborns will turn toward the _____ of a sound. If a man and woman both speak at the same time, newborns will turn toward the _____ voice. Babies respond readily to _____ sounds. _____ _____ and _____ tend to be the favorite sounds of newborns. They also like soft, rhythmic sounds such as the sound of a human _____.

Senses of Smell and Taste:

The senses of smell and taste are _____ _____ at birth. Two or three days after birth, babies will cry and turn their heads away from _____, unpleasant odors. A baby soon learns to recognize his or her _____ by her smell. Babies can tell the difference between _____ within two or three days of birth. Babies will reject a _____ flavor and accept a _____ flavor.

Sense of Feeling:

Newborns can feel changes in _____ at birth. They can also distinguish _____. In the first days after birth, they can feel _____. From the moment of birth, newborns are extremely sensitive to being _____. _____ and _____ have been found to enhance a baby's overall development. Physical contact also tends to strengthen the emotional _____ between baby and parents.

The Newborn's Reflexes

Name _____

Date _____ Period _____

Write the name of the reflex a newborn is using in each of the following descriptions.

_____ 1. This occurs when the outside of the sole of a newborn's foot is stroked. The newborn extends the toes upward and outward.

_____ 2. The newborn reacts to a sudden change of position by throwing the arms apart and extending the legs.

_____ 3. When held upright, a baby raises the sole of the foot when it touches a surface, as if walking.

_____ 4. A newborn closes his or her hand tightly around an object that is placed in the palm.

_____ 5. When the baby's cheek is touched, the baby turns toward the touch.

_____ 6. A newborn arches the back and throws the head back when a loud noise occurs.

_____ 7. The newborn begins to try to find food when the mouth is touched.

_____ 8. The newborn's toes curl around a finger placed on the sole of the foot near the toes.

Explain why nature provides babies with reflexes. _____

_____

_____

_____

_____

_____

_____

_____

_____

_____

_____

_____

_____

_____

_____

_____

_____

_____

_____

Care of the Newborn

Name _____

Date _____ Period _____

Complete the following statements about the care of newborns by filling in the blanks.

1. When holding a newborn, parents should be sure to give firm support to the newborn's _____ and _____.

2. Most newborns sleep about _____ to _____ hours a day.

3. As they sleep, newborns should be _____ and _____.

4. Parents do not need to tiptoe and whisper while their babies are _____.

5. _____ _____ (_____) is a condition in which an infant dies suddenly without warning in his or her sleep.

6. _____ times provide opportunities to enhance parent-child relationships.

7. A breast-feeding mother should remember every substance that enters her body will affect the _____ she produces.

8. If formula-feeding, hold the baby in a _____-_____ position.

9. _____ the baby once during feeding and again after feeding.

10. Newborns need _____ to _____ feedings in a 24-hour period.

11. A baby should be _____ in a room that is warm and free from drafts.

12. _____ leave a baby alone on a table or in a tub.

13. The best way to prevent _____ _____ is to thoroughly wash and rinse the scalp daily.

14. While dressing a baby, parents should take time to _____ with the baby.

15. _____ are the baby's most essential clothing items.

16. In the beginning, newborns use as many as _____ to _____ diapers daily.

17. The key to preventing diaper rash is _____.

18. Generally, it is good for parents to respond promptly and consistently to their newborns' _____.

Choose one statement above. In the space below explain why you agree or disagree with it. Statement # _____

_____

_____

_____

_____

_____

_____

_____

_____

Facts About Newborns

Activity F

Chapter 10

Name _____

Date _____ Period _____

Respond to the following statements. Then discuss each statement in class.

Agree	Disagree	Unsure	
_____	_____	_____	1. When newborns sniffle and sneeze, it means they are sick.
_____	_____	_____	2. A newborn's eyes may cross for a few weeks, but they will correct themselves as they develop.
_____	_____	_____	3. Babies usually lose weight the first few days after birth, but they quickly regain this loss and then continue to grow.
_____	_____	_____	4. In normal light, the newborn sees patterns of light and dark and can distinguish some shapes.
_____	_____	_____	5. A newborn can hear even before birth.
_____	_____	_____	6. The senses of smell and taste are not well developed at birth.
_____	_____	_____	7. Newborns are unable to feel changes in temperature at birth.
_____	_____	_____	8. When a baby's position is changed suddenly or when the baby hears a sudden loud noise, the Babinski reflex can be seen.
_____	_____	_____	9. When parents hold and talk to their baby, this communication encourages the baby's intellectual and social development.
_____	_____	_____	10. Newborns usually sleep through the night without waking up.
_____	_____	_____	11. The most important factor in the choice between breast- or bottle-feeding is the attitude of the parents.
_____	_____	_____	12. Babies are adaptable and will learn to sleep through ordinary household noises.
_____	_____	_____	13. Tub baths are usually given until the stub of the umbilical cord drops off and the navel heals.
_____	_____	_____	14. Disposable diapers are better than cloth diapers.
_____	_____	_____	15. Answering cries promptly and consistently will spoil newborns.

I most strongly agree with statement #_____ because _____

_____

_____

I most strongly disagree with statement #_____ because_____

_____

_____

_____

Personal Adjustments

Name _____

Date _____ Period _____

Survey parents about the personal adjustments they had to make when their baby was born. Share and compare your results with members of your class. Think about the survey responses. Then answer the following questions.

1. How did the birth of your baby affect your role as a husband or wife?

_____

_____

_____

2. How do you share in the responsibilities for the care of your baby?

_____

_____

_____

3. How has your baby affected routines?

_____

_____

_____

4. How has your baby affected your finances?

_____

_____

_____

5. How has your baby affected your relationship with your spouse?

_____

_____

_____

After comparing the responses to the above questions with those obtained by other members of your class, answer the following question.

Why is a healthy husband-wife relationship a strong foundation for building a happy family?

_____

_____

_____

_____

_____

_____

_____

11 Parents and Their Infants

Large and Small Motor Skills

Activity A

Chapter 11

Name _____

Date _____ Period _____

Some of the highlights of large and small motor skills that usually develop during the first year are listed below. Number them in the sequence in which they occur by placing the letters in the appropriate blanks.

Sequence of Development   **Large Motor Skills**

1. _____ A. Babies walk holding onto a parent's hand.

2. _____ B. Babies crawl.

3. _____ C. Babies can sit with slight support.

4. _____ D. Newborns lie curled in a fetal position.

5. _____ E. Babies attempt to climb stairs.

6. _____ F. Babies first attempt to pull themselves to a standing position.

7. _____ G. Babies can keep their backs firm and their heads steady when propped in a sitting position for a short time.

8. _____ H. As babies gain more control of their neck muscles, they can hold up their heads.

9. _____ I. The first steps alone are wobbly, with hands held high for balance.

10. _____ J. Babies can hold their heads higher and for a longer time when they bend their arms for supports.

11. _____ K. Babies can sit without support.

12. _____ L. Babies can raise their chests, supporting themselves with straight arms.

13. _____ M. Babies will stand whenever possible and cruise around furniture.

Sequence of Development   **Small Motor Skills**

1. _____ A. Babies begin to swipe at objects, such as a cradle gym.

2. _____ B. Babies begin eating with their fingers.

3. _____ C. Babies grasp objects in reflex movements, but grasps are becoming voluntary.

4. _____ D. Babies can use index finger to point.

5. _____ E. Babies begin to use mitten grasp for grabbing objects.

6. _____ F. Babies keep hands fisted or slightly opened.

7. _____ G. Babies may show preferences for one hand.

8. _____ H. Babies learn to use the pincer grasp.

9. _____ I. Babies begin to grasp objects with thumb and fingers.

10. _____ J. Babies can take off shoes and socks.

Dangers and Safeguards for Infants

Activity B

Chapter 11

Name _____

Date _____ Period _____

Indicate which of the following are dangers and safeguards. If the statement is a danger, write **D** in the blank. Then identify the danger and explain how it could be avoided. If the statement is a safeguard, write **S** in the blank and explain why it is a safe practice.

_____ 1. Tom's daughter, Joy, is in the stage of pulling herself to a standing position. Tom has removed all tables and chairs that are not stable.

_____

_____

_____ 2. When buying a playpen and crib for their grandchild, Betty and Jim made sure the slats were no more than 2 ⅜ inches (6 cm) apart.

_____

_____

_____ 3. When riding in a car, Valerie holds her baby on her lap.

_____

_____

_____ 4. Carmela's parents keep all doors closed or doorways blocked with secure barriers.

_____

_____

_____ 5. Don leaves his six-month-old son John alone in the bathtub while he quickly answers the telephone.

_____

_____

_____ 6. While visiting relatives, Dezaree places her baby, Andre, in the middle of a bed for a nap. She places a barrier around the bed in case Andre wakes up or rolls over.

_____

_____

_____ 7. Tyrone placed covers over the unused electrical sockets in his home.

_____

_____

_____ 8. Jane props her infant son's bottle in a bottle holder so she can continue washing clothes.

_____

_____

Intellectual Development

Activity C

Name _____

Chapter 11

Date _____ Period _____

Some of the highlights of intellectual development that usually occur during the first year are listed below. Read each statement and explain the meaning of each. Then give an example of how each form of development might be observed in an infant's behavior.

1. Babies can anticipate a whole object by seeing only a part of it. _____

_____

_____

_____

_____

_____

2. Babies begin to make simple associations. _____

_____

_____

_____

_____

_____

3. Babies learn the concept of object permanence. _____

_____

_____

_____

_____

_____

4. Babies become good imitators. _____

_____

_____

_____

_____

_____

5. Babies become aware of the differences among people and associate certain behaviors with certain people.

_____

_____

_____

_____

_____

Emotional and Social Development

Activity D

Chapter 11

Name _____

Date _____ Period _____

Some of the highlights of emotional and social development that usually occur during the first year are listed below. Read each statement. Then describe how a parent might handle each of these aspects of an infant's development.

1. As they become more active and more social, babies may have trouble settling down to sleep. _____

_____

_____

_____

_____

_____

2. Babies may form an attachment to one special toy. _____

_____

_____

_____

_____

_____

3. Babies' favorite games are those that involve other people. _____

_____

_____

_____

_____

_____

4. Babies' new walking skills may create emotional tensions. _____

_____

_____

_____

_____

_____

5. Babies' fear of strangers increases. _____

_____

_____

_____

_____

_____

Infant Crossword

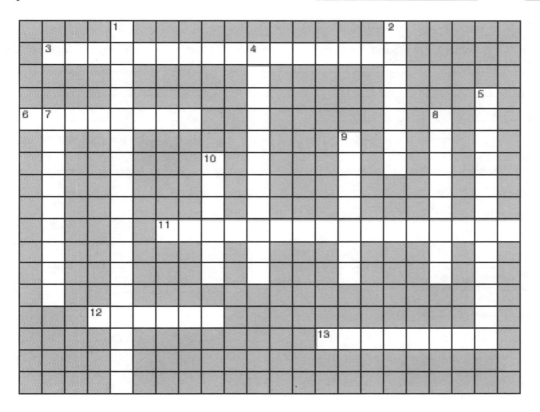

Across

3. _____ _____ is the concept that unseen objects have not necessarily disappeared.

6. Their developing _____ help babies learn to recognize family members and familiar objects and sounds.

11. The _____ is the person who spends the most time with the baby.

12. A refined grasp in which objects are picked up with just the thumb and forefinger is called the _____ grasp.

13. _____ development includes growing in height, weight, and muscle control.

Down

1. The overwhelming fear shown by infants when the primary caregiver is not in sight is called _____ _____.

2. _____ is the phasing out of taking milk from a breast or bottle.

4. The _____ _____ is made with the palm and fingers opposing the thumb.

5. _____ development refers to the development of a person's mental and thinking abilities.

7. _____ development involves recognition and expression of feelings and emotions.

8. To ease minor _____ discomfort, parents can let the baby chew on a boiled-clean cloth that won't shred.

9. Hand manipulation skills are dependent upon _____ -_____ coordination and muscle development.

10. _____ development is the process of learning to relate to other people.

Caring for Infants

Complete the following statements about caring for infants.

1. When babies first start eating solid foods, parents shouldn't worry about how much food is actually eaten because _____

    _____

    _____

2. It is not a good idea for parents to give their baby a bottle when they put the baby to bed because _____

    _____

    _____

3. To ease minor teething discomfort, parents can_____

    _____

    _____

4. Parents can help babies learn the meaning of words by _____

    _____

    _____

5. At bedtime, parents can help babies make the transition from daytime activity to nighttime sleep by _____

    _____

    _____

6. After enforcing a *no*, parents can help prevent further naughty behavior by _____

    _____

    _____

7. Parents should not sneak away while babies are busy playing because _____

    _____

    _____

8. In order to handle separation anxiety when a parent must leave, the parent should_____

    _____

    _____

9. Upon arrival, when visiting a strange place with their babies, parents should _____

    _____

    _____

    _____

Observing an Infant

Activity G   Name _____

Chapter 11   Date _____ Period _____

Observe an infant for at least 30 minutes. Find out the following information and record your observations below. Discuss your observations in class. Then compare your observations with those of other class members and with the child development charts in the text.

Infant _____ Age _____ (months) Gender _____

General description of infant: _____

_____

Where observation took place: _____

When observation took place: _____

Others present (parents, other children): _____

_____

Physical Development

(Check one): _____ Infant's movements are due to reflexes.

                 _____ Infant's movements are voluntary.

List examples of infant's movements. _____

_____

_____

Describe this infant's large motor skills. _____

_____

_____

From observing this infant, list examples that illustrate large motor skill development. _____

_____

_____

Describe this infant's small motor skills. _____

_____

_____

From observing this infant, list examples that illustrate small motor skill development. _____

_____

_____

(Continued)

Name _____

Intellectual Development

Describe this infant's general intellectual development. _____
_____

_____

From observing this infant, list examples that illustrate this._____
_____

_____

Describe this infant's language development._____
_____

_____

From observing this infant, list examples that illustrate this._____
_____

_____

Emotional and Social Development

Describe this infant's emotional development._____
_____

_____

From observing this infant, list examples that illustrate this._____
_____

_____

Describe this infant's social development. _____
_____

_____

From observing this infant, list examples that illustrate this._____
_____

_____

12 Parents and Their Toddlers

Observing a Toddler

Activity A

Chapter 12

Name _____

Date _____ Period _____

Observe a toddler for at least 30 minutes. Find out the following information and record your observations below. Discuss your observations in class. Then compare your observations with those of other class members and with the child development charts in the text.

Toddler _____ Age _____ (months) Gender _____

General description of toddler: _____

_____

Where observation took place: _____

When observation took place: _____

Others present (parents, other children, etc.): _____

_____

Physical Development

List examples of toddler's movements. _____

_____

_____

Describe this toddler's large motor skills. _____

_____

_____

From observing this toddler, list examples that illustrate large motor skill development. _____

_____

_____

Describe this toddler's small motor skills. _____

_____

_____

From observing this toddler, list examples that illustrate small motor skill development. _____

_____

_____

(Continued)

From observing this toddler, list examples of life skills that have been mastered. _____

_____

_____

Intellectual Development

Describe this toddler's general intellectual development. _____

_____

_____

From observing this toddler, list examples that illustrate this. _____

_____

_____

Describe this toddler's language development. _____

_____

_____

From observing this toddler, list examples that illustrate this. _____

_____

_____

Emotional and Social Development

Describe this toddler's emotional development. _____

_____

_____

From observing this toddler, list examples that illustrate this. _____

_____

_____

Describe this toddler's social development. _____

_____

_____

From observing this toddler, list examples that illustrate this. _____

_____

_____

Keeping Toddlers Safe

Name _____

Date _____ Period _____

Certain items and situations can pose a danger to toddlers. Describe what you would do to protect toddlers from each of the following hazards.

1. Windows and doors: _____

_____

_____

2. Stoves, pots, and pans: _____

_____

_____

3. Unsafe toys and stuffed animals (be specific): _____

_____

_____

4. Car travel: _____

_____

_____

5. Street traffic: _____

_____

_____

6. Pets: _____

_____

_____

7. Poisons, cleaning agents, and medicines: _____

_____

_____

8. Sharp objects: _____

_____

_____

Life Skills of Toddlers

Activity C

Chapter 12

Name _____

Date _____ Period _____

Read the following case studies. Then determine whether each represents a desirable or undesirable way for parents to teach their toddlers life skills. Explain your answers.

Case #1   *Eighteen-month-old Amy likes to feed herself. Amy's father, Bill, ties a bib on her and seats her in the high chair. He puts a small amount of bite-size green beans and ground meat on her plate. As Amy eats, he adds a little more food to her plate. Bill then puts applesauce on her plate and hands Amy her spoon. With a great deal of effort, Amy manages to eat almost as much as she spills. Bill then pours a small amount of milk in a small plastic mug, and Amy successfully drinks the milk. By this time Amy is finished eating. Bill allows her to leave the table to play while the rest of the family finishes their meal.*

Desirable or undesirable? _____

Explain. _____

_____

_____

_____

_____

_____

_____

_____

_____

_____

Case #2   *Pam is worried about her two-year-old daughter, Michelle. At mealtime, Pam fills Michelle's plate full of food. Michelle eats very little of the food. She begins to cry and wants to play with her toys. Pam does not allow Michelle to leave the table until the rest of the family has finished eating. Michelle's crying makes mealtimes unpleasant for the rest of the family. Later, Michelle is hungry and wants a snack. Pam gives her a cookie.*

Desirable or undesirable? _____

Explain. _____

_____

_____

_____

_____

_____

_____

_____

_____

(Continued)

Case #3   Juan is very proud of himself. He has just put a shirt on all by himself. He runs to show his father, Jose. Jose begins to laugh at his son. Jose tells Juan the shirt is on backward and a purple shirt doesn't look good with green pants. Juan begins to cry. Jose tells him not to be a baby.

Desirable or undesirable? _____

Explain. _____

_____

_____

_____

_____

_____

_____

_____

_____

_____

_____

Case #4   Keisha wants to wash her own face and hands, but she cannot reach the sink. Her mother, Sonya, gives her a short stool that helps Keisha reach the sink. When Keisha does not remove all the soap from her face, Sonya gently shows her how with a washcloth. Sonya praises Keisha for her clean face and hands.

Desirable or undesirable? _____

Explain. _____

_____

_____

_____

_____

_____

_____

_____

_____

_____

_____

_____

_____

(Continued)

Case #5   Sixteen-month-old Timmy watches as his father, Bob, brushes his teeth. Timmy wants to brush his teeth, too. Bob doesn't think it is necessary for Timmy to brush his teeth since he will be losing his baby teeth in a few years.

Desirable or undesirable? _____

Explain. _____

_____

_____

_____

_____

_____

_____

_____

_____

_____

_____

_____

Case #6   Cassandra is almost two years old. Her mother, Helen, wants to toilet train Cassandra by the time she is two. Helen forces her to sit on the potty chair for long periods of time. When Cassandra has accidents, Helen punishes her.

Desirable or undesirable? _____

Explain. _____

_____

_____

_____

_____

_____

_____

_____

_____

_____

_____

_____

_____

Teachable Moments

Name _____

Date _____ Period _____

Think of four examples of teachable moments that parents could have with their children. Fill in the chart below describing situations when parents could stimulate the physical, intellectual, emotional, or social learning of their children.

Family Members in Scene	Situation or Setting	Type of Development Enhanced (Physical, Intellectual, Social, Emotional)	What Was Learned?
1.			
2.			

(Continued)

Family Members in Scene	Situation or Setting	Type of Development Enhanced (Physical, Intellectual, Social, Emotional)	What Was Learned?
3.			
4.			

Helping Toddlers Learn Their Limits

Activity E

Chapter 12

Name _____

Date _____ Period _____

Indicate whether you agree or disagree with the following statements. Then discuss them in class.

Agree   Disagree

_____   _____   1. Children need to be taught behavioral boundaries and limits.

_____   _____   2. Children should be told what is expected of them.

_____   _____   3. Parents should let their children know what they can do as well as what they cannot do.

_____   _____   4. Limits should be flexible to meet particular needs or events.

_____   _____   5. Toddlers need to learn they cannot always have their own way.

_____   _____   6. Children should be allowed to feel their ideas and desires are worthwhile.

_____   _____   7. Parents should not offer a choice when there is no choice available.

_____   _____   8. Toddlers expect firmness and caring guidance.

_____   _____   9. Parents should use slight spankings to reinforce their stands on rare occasions.

_____   _____   10. Parents should use psychological approaches to reinforce their standards.

_____   _____   11. The role of guidance is to achieve results without being abusive.

_____   _____   12. Discipline that is right for one child may be too strong for a more sensitive child.

_____   _____   13. Firm limits allow toddlers to sense their parents care about them.

_____   _____   14. Parents should establish limits but give their toddlers guidelines and freedom within those limits.

_____   _____   15. Parents can help their children avoid temper tantrums by meeting their children's reasonable needs.

Choose a statement from the checklist above. Explain why you strongly agree or strongly disagree with that statement.

I strongly (agree/disagree) with statement number _____ because _____

_____

_____

_____

_____

_____

_____

_____

_____

_____

_____

Handling Toddlers' Behavior

Activity F

Chapter 12

Name _____

Date _____ Period _____

The following typical behaviors may challenge parents during the "terrible two's." Describe how you would handle each of the following behaviors. Compare your responses to those of other class members and discuss them in class.

1. Attachment to a favorite object: _____

_____

_____

2. Separation anxiety: _____

_____

_____

_____

_____

_____

3. Behavior conflicts, such as refusing to go to bed: _____

_____

_____

_____

_____

_____

_____

_____

_____

4. Temper tantrums: _____

_____

_____

_____

_____

_____

_____

_____

_____

_____

_____

Selecting Toys for Toddlers

Activity G

Chapter 12

Name _____

Date _____ Period _____

Pretend you are choosing toys for toddlers. Visit a store that sells toys. Inspect the toys. In the spaces provided, sketch or clip and attach catalog photos of toys that would promote the physical, intellectual, emotional, and social development of toddlers. Then complete the checklist and evaluate the toy.

Toy that would promote physical development in toddlers:

Describe how this toy could help promote physical development in toddlers.

_____

_____

_____

Use this checklist to evaluate the toy.

	Yes	No	Does not apply
Is it durable?			
Is it easily cleaned or washable?			
Are small parts such as eyes and wheels securely attached?			
Is it free of sharp edges, points, or splinters?			
Is it made of nonflammable materials?			
Is the paint nontoxic and lead-free?			
Is it colorful?			
Does it teach new skills?			
Is it nonviolent?			
Does it encourage interaction?			
Is it appropriate for the child's developmental level?			
Does it encourage the use of imagination?			

Based on this evaluation, is this toy a good choice for toddlers? Explain why or why not.

_____

_____

_____

_____

(Continued)

Toy that would promote intellectual development in toddlers:

(blank box)

Describe how this toy could help promote intellectual development in toddlers.

_____

_____

_____

Use this checklist to evaluate the toy.

	Yes	No	Does not apply
Is it durable?			
Is it easily cleaned or washable?			
Are small parts such as eyes and wheels securely attached?			
Is it free of sharp edges, points, or splinters?			
Is it made of nonflammable materials?			
Is the paint nontoxic and lead-free?			
Is it colorful?			
Does it teach new skills?			
Is it nonviolent?			
Does it encourage interaction?			
Is it appropriate for the child's developmental level?			
Does it encourage the use of imagination?			

Based on this evaluation, is this toy a good choice for toddlers? Explain why or why not.

_____

_____

_____

_____

_____

(Continued)

Toy that would promote social and emotional development in toddlers:

Describe how this toy could help promote social and emotional development in toddlers.

_____

_____

_____

Use this checklist to evaluate the toy.

	Yes	No	Does not apply
Is it durable?			
Is it easily cleaned or washable?			
Are small parts such as eyes and wheels securely attached?			
Is it free of sharp edges, points, or splinters?			
Is it made of nonflammable materials?			
Is the paint nontoxic and lead-free?			
Is it colorful?			
Does it teach new skills?			
Is it nonviolent?			
Does it encourage interaction?			
Is it appropriate for the child's developmental level?			
Does it encourage the use of imagination?			

Based on this evaluation, is this toy a good choice for toddlers? Explain why or why not.

_____

_____

_____

_____

_____

_____

Books for Children

Name _____

Date_____ Period _____

When parents introduce children to books at an early age, children learn to enjoy books and value them. Visit the library and select a book you feel would be appropriate to share with a toddler. Read the book to a toddler and then answer the following questions.

Title of book:_____

Briefly describe the story.

_____

_____

_____

_____

Age of child: _____

Where and when book was read: _____

Were plenty of pictures provided to allow the child to "read" the pictures? _____

Did the book contain big, colorful, detailed illustrations? _____

Could the child follow the story by looking at the pictures? _____

Did the story hold the child's interest? _____

List any questions the child had during or after the story and your answers to these questions.

_____

_____

_____

_____

_____

Child's overall reaction to the book:_____

_____

_____

_____

_____

_____

Based upon your responses above, would you recommend this book to parents of toddlers? Explain why or why not.

_____

_____

_____

_____

_____

13 Parents and Their Preschoolers

Observing a Preschooler

Activity A

Chapter 13

Name _____

Date _____ Period _____

Observe a preschooler for at least 30 minutes. Find out the following information and record your observations below. Discuss your observations in class. Then compare your observations with those of other class members and with the child development charts in the text.

Preschooler _____ Age _____ Gender _____

General description of preschooler: _____

_____

_____

_____

Where observation took place: _____

When observation took place: _____

Others present (parents, other children, child care worker): _____

_____

Physical Development

List examples of preschooler's movements. _____

_____

_____

_____

Describe this preschooler's large motor skills. _____

_____

_____

_____

From observing this preschooler, list examples that illustrate large motor skill development. _____

_____

_____

_____

(Continued)

Describe this preschooler's small motor skills. _____

_____

_____

From observing this preschooler, list examples that illustrate small motor skills development. _____

_____

_____

_____

From observing this preschooler, list examples of life skills that have been mastered. _____

_____

_____

_____

Intellectual Development

Describe this preschooler's general intellectual development. _____

_____

_____

From observing this preschooler, list examples that illustrate this. _____

_____

_____

Describe this preschooler's language development. _____

_____

_____

_____

From observing this preschooler, list examples that illustrate this. _____

_____

_____

_____

(Continued)

●

Describe this preschooler's math and reading skills. _____

_____

_____

_____

From observing this preschooler, list examples that illustrate this. _____

_____

_____

_____

Emotional and Social Development

Describe this preschooler's emotional development. _____

_____

_____

_____

From observing this preschooler, list examples that illustrate this. _____

_____

_____

_____

●

Describe this preschooler's social development. _____

_____

_____

_____

From observing this preschooler, list examples that illustrate this. _____

_____

_____

_____

●

Reasoning with Preschoolers

Name _____

Date _____ Period _____

Read the following statements. If the statement describes a positive way of reasoning with preschoolers, write **P** in the blank. If the statement describes a negative way of reasoning with preschoolers, write **N** in the blank. Then write two more positive statements and two more negative statements of your own.

_____ 1. Let preschoolers know what you expect of them, keeping in mind individual capabilities to meet these expectations.

_____ 2. Let children know what they can do and do not dwell on what they cannot do.

_____ 3. Sarcastically belittle children so they will feel bad and try to do things right.

_____ 4. Use expectations that show confidence in children.

_____ 5. Use verbal abuse to make children do things correctly.

_____ 6. Withdraw love and affection as a means of getting back at children if they have done something wrong.

_____ 7. If children do something wrong, punish them physically or isolate them to teach them a lesson.

_____ 8. Solve problems with children by guiding them to find solutions.

P 9. _____

_____

_____

P 10. _____

_____

_____

N 11. _____

_____

_____

N 12. _____

_____

_____

Life Skills of Preschoolers

Activity C

Chapter 13

Name _____

Date _____ Period _____

Read the following case studies. Then determine whether each represents a desirable or undesirable way for parents to teach their preschoolers life skills. Explain your answers.

Case #1   *Matthew is four. His mother, Carmen, takes him with her on shopping trips to the grocery store. She allows Matthew to choose the cereal he wants for breakfast. She also allows him to help her choose the fruits he will eat for snacks. Matthew's father, Tony, grows vegetables in the garden. Tony lets Matthew help him care for the garden. Tony also allows Matthew to pick and help clean the vegetables they will have for dinner. Carmen and Tony have very few problems with Matthew at mealtime.*

Desirable or undesirable? _____

Explain. _____

_____

_____

_____

_____

_____

_____

_____

_____

_____

Case #2   *Danny loves to play outside. He often comes in with dirty clothes and hands just before he is supposed to go somewhere with Don, his father. Don pulls Danny into the bathroom and roughly scrubs Danny's face and pulls a comb through his hair. Danny cries and says, "I don't care if I ever look good."*

Desirable or undesirable? _____

Explain. _____

_____

_____

_____

_____

_____

_____

_____

_____

_____

(Continued)

Case #3   *Three-year-old Dana wants to dress herself. Dana's mother, Marilyn, realizes extra time will be needed, so she makes sure Dana starts early. Occasionally Dana will put a blouse on backward or her shoes on the wrong feet. When this happens, Marilyn gives Dana clues so she will learn how to dress. If Dana feels frustrated or discouraged, Marilyn reassures her by saying, "You can do it."*

Desirable or undesirable? _____

Explain. _____

_____

_____

_____

_____

_____

_____

_____

_____

_____

_____

_____

Case #4   *Tinaka is five. Her parents, Mikio and Coy, were just divorced and are concerned about their problems. Tinaka lives with her mother during the week and with her father on weekends. Recently Tinaka has begun wetting the bed every night. When she was four years old, she seldom had an accident at night. When Tinaka wets the bed, Mikio punishes her and Coy calls her a baby.*

Desirable or undesirable? _____

Explain. _____

_____

_____

_____

_____

_____

_____

_____

_____

_____

_____

_____

_____

Intellectual Development Concepts

Name _____

Date _____ Period _____

Interact with some preschoolers. Give an example to illustrate each of the following statements related to intellectual development.

Concept	Example
1. Preschoolers do not simply accept ready-made concepts and principles.	
2. Preschoolers are keenly aware of their environment and study it with all their senses.	
3. Preschoolers are intent upon finding out how everything works.	
4. Preschoolers are learning the concept of cause and effect.	
5. Preschoolers have vivid imaginations, and the fine line between fact and fantasy may be hazy.	
6. The concept of time is still difficult for preschoolers to understand.	
7. Preschoolers know right from wrong and learn they may be punished if they disobey.	
8. Symbolic thinking allows preschoolers to use materials around them in interesting ways.	

Children's Play

Activity E

Chapter 13

Name _____

Date _____ Period _____

Play changes as children grow older in terms of how children interact with other children in a play situation. Describe each of the following stages of play. Tell the age (infants, toddlers, preschoolers) at which each is likely to first be observed. Then give an example of each of the forms of play. (Information from both chapters 12 and 13 of the text can be used to complete this activity.)

What do children learn from play? _____

_____

_____

_____

_____

_____

Parallel Play

Description: _____

_____

Age group when first observed: _____

Example: _____

_____

_____

_____

Alternate Play

Description: _____

_____

Age group when first observed: _____

Example: _____

_____

_____

_____

Cooperative Play

Description: _____

_____

Age group when first observed: _____

Example: _____

_____

_____

_____

14 Parents and Their School-Age Children

School-Age Children

Activity A

Chapter 14

Name _____

Date _____ Period _____

Complete general descriptive statements about school-age children. Compare your statements with those of other class members and discuss them in class. (Keep in mind that every child is a unique individual and these are descriptions about school-age children in general.)

Most six-year-olds are_____

_____

_____

Most seven-year-olds are _____

_____

_____

Most eight-year-olds are _____

_____

_____

Most nine-year-olds are_____

_____

_____

Most ten-year-olds are_____

_____

_____

Most eleven-year-olds are _____

_____

_____

Most twelve-year-olds are_____

_____

_____

Children and Sports

Name _____

Date_____ Period _____

Pretend you are the parent of a school-age child interested in participating in sports. Indicate which of the following statements would be good guidelines to follow by placing a check in the appropriate blank.

_____ 1. Children under 6 years of age should be encouraged to participate in competitive sports.

_____ 2. Any child who is injured or in pain should be removed from the game and given prompt attention.

_____ 3. A child's athletic ability should be compared to that of a brother or sister.

_____ 4. Children between the ages of 6 and 8 should be restricted to noncontact sports such as swimming, tennis, and running.

_____ 5. A first-aid kit should be kept nearby, and the coach should know how to use it.

_____ 6. Parents need to push their children into sports.

_____ 7. Rather than criticize their children for mistakes, parents should offer praise for any effort or improvement.

_____ 8. Contact sports such as soccer, basketball, and wrestling are recommended for children over 8 years old.

_____ 9. Good coaches place more emphasis on winning than on the children's welfare.

_____ 10. If parents disagree with the calls of the officials at a game, they should argue with them.

_____ 11. Tackle football and other collision sports should not be played by children under the age of 10.

_____ 12. The facilities for practices and games should be in good condition.

_____ 13. Protective equipment, if needed for the sport, should be available and used regularly.

_____ 14. Children should be punished if they strike out or drop a crucial pass.

_____ 15. When watching a game, parents should let the coaches do the coaching and players do the playing.

_____ 16. Parents should help their children realize trying hard, playing well, and enjoying the game are more accurate measures of success than just winning or losing.

How do you feel about children participating in competitive sports? _____

_____

_____

_____

_____

_____

_____

_____

Intellectual Achievements and Teachable Moments

Name _____

Date _____ Period _____

Various intellectual achievements of the school-age years are listed below. Pretend you are a parent. List examples of teachable moments or activities that you could use to help your children master these intellectual achievements.

Intellectual Achievements	Examples
Multiple classification	
Seriation	
Conservation	
Reversibility	

Facts About School-Age Children

Activity D

Chapter 14

Name _____

Date _____ Period _____

Complete the following statements. If a statement is true, write *T* in the blank. If a statement is false, write *F* in the blank.

_____ 1. Parents should pressure their children to learn.

_____ 2. Near the end of the school-age period, girls and boys have marked differences in their physical development.

_____ 3. Through athletics, children can learn to appreciate physical fitness, respect law and authority, and cooperate with others.

_____ 4. Sports have the potential for both physical and psychological damage.

_____ 5. School-age children are too young to be warned about kidnapping and sexual abuse.

_____ 6. In stores and shopping malls, parents should keep an eye on their children at all times.

_____ 7. Children's interest in schoolwork is often affected by their peer relationships.

_____ 8. School-age children refine their classifying skills by collecting and identifying things.

_____ 9. The ability to order groups of things by size, weight, age, or any common property is called *conservation*.

_____ 10. Middle childhood is an age of activity and investigation.

_____ 11. Because of their high activity levels, children need an adequate breakfast even more than adults.

_____ 12. Success or failure in reading has no effect upon other areas of learning.

_____ 13. Art, drama, and music activities provide children with expressive outlets for their emotions.

_____ 14. During the school years, children become more socially independent.

_____ 15. Group activities among children of the same gender are popular throughout the school-age years.

_____ 16. During the later years of the school-age period, many children reach puberty and go through emotional changes.

_____ 17. It is not necessary for parents to be aware of friendships their children are forming.

_____ 18. When possible, parents should allow children to invite their friends home.

_____ 19. Children resent parents butting into their lives with demands concerning their selection of friends.

_____ 20. As children near the end of the school-age period, their intense desire for conformity may begin to upset their parents.

Observing a School-Age Child

Activity E

Chapter 14

Name _____

Date _____ Period _____

Observe a school-age child for at least 30 minutes. Find out the following information and record your observations below. Discuss your observations in class. Then compare your observations with those of other class members and with the child development charts in the text.

Child _____ Age _____ Gender _____

General description of child: _____

_____

Where observation took place: _____

When observation took place: _____

Others present (parents, other children, etc.) _____

_____

Physical Development

Describe the physical appearance of the child. _____

_____

_____

Describe particular physical skills of the child (activeness, coordination, etc.). _____

_____

_____

_____

From observing the child, list examples that illustrate this. _____

_____

_____

_____

Intellectual Development

List concepts the child appears to have mastered. _____

_____

From observing the child, list examples that illustrate this. _____

_____

_____

List the child's interests. _____

_____

_____

(Continued)

Describe the child's vocabulary. _____

_____

_____

Describe the child's attention span. _____

_____

_____

Emotional and Social Development

Describe the child's emotional development. _____

_____

_____

From observing the child, list examples that illustrate this. _____

_____

_____

Describe the child's social development. _____

_____

_____

From observing the child, list examples that illustrate this. _____

_____

_____

_____

School Adjustments

Name _____

Date _____ Period _____

In each of the following situations, pretend you are a parent of the school-age child described. Your child has brought home the following notes from his or her teacher. Suggest ways you might help your child adjust to school in each of these situations.

> Dear Parent:
>
> Jordan says in the rush to get ready for school, he must often skip breakfast. He often lacks the energy to participate fully in class.
>
> M. Jones

_____

_____

_____

_____

_____

> Dear Parent:
>
> Tyler has difficulty reading.
>
> Mr. Caldwell

_____

_____

_____

_____

_____

> Dear Parent:
>
> Veliscia's writing is not readable.
>
> Mrs. Soto

_____

_____

_____

_____

_____

(Continued)

Dear Parent:

Rachel's papers are seldom done neatly.

Ms. Wilson

Dear Parent:

Alan is having trouble in history because his reading skills are not good.

M. Kim

Dear Parent:

Jose is having difficulty with math.

Mrs. M. Smith

(Continued)

Dear Parent:

Vaneshi expresses very little interest in science.

Ms. Khan

Dear Parent:

Jeremy has difficulty expressing his feelings.

Mr. Wong

Dear Parent:

Kayla does not do her homework.

Mr. Rodriguez

Self-Care Children

Name _____

Date _____ Period _____

Respond to the following questions and statements about self-care children.

1. What is a self-care child? _____

   _____

   _____

2. Pretend you are a working parent. Describe your child. Then list guidelines you would want your child to follow until you return home from work.

   Child: _____ Age: _____ Maturity: _____

   Household and safety rules (activities child may and may not do when parents are not home):

   _____

   _____

   _____

   _____

   _____

   _____

   _____

   _____

   _____

   _____

   Describe actions you would want your child to follow if he or she were home alone during the following emergencies:

   A fire_____

   _____

   A storm _____

   _____

   An illness _____

   _____

   Phone numbers child should know: _____

   _____

3. List after-school programs, telephone programs, and support groups available for self-care children in your area.

   _____

   _____

   _____

   _____

   _____

Children and Stress

Name _____

Date _____ Period _____

Complete the following exercises about children and stress.

Pretend you are a school-age child. List eight examples of stress you might experience.

_____

_____

_____

_____

_____

_____

_____

_____

_____

Now pretend you are the parent of a school-age child. From the list above, describe how you would help your child deal with each stress.

_____

_____

_____

_____

_____

_____

_____

_____

_____

_____

_____

_____

_____

_____

_____

_____

_____

Medical Checkups for School-Age Children

Activity I

Chapter 14

Name _____

Date _____ Period _____

Complete the following exercises regarding medical care for school-age children.

Pretend you are the parent of a school-age child. List five questions you might ask the doctor during a routine medical checkup.

_____

_____

_____

_____

_____

Contact your school district's nurse or the health department. Find out what immunizations are required by your school district and why.

Required Immunization	Reason

Pretend you are a health care professional. Explain why the following are important for school-age children.

Sports physicals: _____

_____

Eye exam: _____

_____

Hearing tests:_____

_____

Dental exam: _____

_____

15 Parents and Their Teens

Smoking

Activity A

Chapter 15

Name _____

Date _____ Period _____

Parents can help their teens make decisions about smoking. Pretend you are the parent of a teen. Complete the following exercises with the responses you would **want** your teen to give.

1. If I develop a serious health problem due to smoking, I can place the blame for this on

    _____ myself

    _____ my parents

    _____ my friends

    _____ society

2. Place the letters in the blanks to rank the following reasons people decide to smoke:

    (A) makes them look older (B) allows them to join a peer group (C) relaxes them (D) gives them something to do with their hands (E) their parents, brothers, or sisters smoked (F) makes them feel good (G) lets them kill time when bored (H) helps them cope with problems (I) a way to get back at parents or authority figures who are telling them not to smoke

Most influential _____ _____ _____ _____ _____ _____ _____ _____ _____ Least influential

3. What would you consider an effective way to discourage teens from smoking? Place the letters in the blanks to indicate your response.

    (A) provide education concerning the health hazards (B) support more stringent laws controlling the sale of cigarettes to minors (C) support more stringent laws concerning smoking areas in public places, schools, etc. (D) order them not to smoke (E) allow them to make up their own minds

Most effective _____ _____ _____ _____ _____ _____ _____ _____ _____ Least effective

4. What do you consider the greatest risk of smoking?

    Lung cancer; breathing problems; heart problems; coughing; bad breath; yellow teeth

    Greatest risk _____

    _____

    _____

    _____

    _____

    Least risk _____

(Continued)

5. If you could vote for a law banning smoking, how would you vote?

I would vote to ban smoking because _____

_____

I would vote to allow smoking because _____

_____

6. Is smoking worth the expense? List the price of one pack of cigarettes. $ _____

Cost if you smoke: 1 pack per day $_____ × 365 days = $ _____

2 packs per day $_____ × 365 days = $ _____

Cost of smoking for: one year $ _____   five years $ _____   20 years $ _____

two years $ _____   10 years $ _____   40 years $ _____

List the cost of four items you wish you could afford to buy in the future. Compare these with the costs of smoking.

_____   _____

_____   _____

How do you want to spend your money? _____

_____

_____

_____

_____

_____

_____

_____

_____

_____

Drinking

Name _____

Date _____ Period _____

Parents can help their teens make decisions about drinking. Pretend you are the parent of a teen. Complete the following exercises with the responses you would **want** your teen to give.

1. If I develop problems with drinking, I can place the blame for them on

    _____ myself

    _____ my parents

    _____ my friends

    _____ society

2. Rank the following, indicating your answer to this statement: "I consider drinking most dangerous when…"

    Driving; at home alone; when emotionally upset; at a party; while babysitting

    Most dangerous _____

    _____

    _____

    _____

    Least dangerous _____

3. If you were at a party and you knew spiked punch was being served, would you drink the punch in order to go along with the crowd?

    Yes, because _____

    No, because _____

    What are the dangers of spiked punch? _____

    _____

4. If the person who drove you to a party was drinking heavily, would you ask someone else to take you home, or would you feel you had to go home with the person who brought you?

    I would let someone else take me home because_____

    _____

    I would go home with the person who brought me because _____

    _____

5. If you could vote for a law to change the legal drinking age, how would you vote?

    To raise the drinking age, because _____

    _____

    To lower the drinking age, because _____

    _____

(Continued)

6. If you were with a group of friends and they decided to see who could drink the most, what would you do?

_____ assume a superior attitude and refuse to drink

_____ say "No, thank you" and say nothing to those who are drinking

_____ drink a little and pretend to be enjoying it

_____ keep up with the crowd

_____ excuse yourself and find a way home

_____ Other:

7. Rank the following, indicating your answer to this statement: "If I felt I had a drinking problem, the first person I would consult would be…"

Parent; religious leader; friend; physician; member of alcoholics anonymous; school counselor

First to consult _____

_____

_____

_____

Last to consult _____

8. If teens see their parents drink, it affects their decisions about using alcohol.

I agree because _____

_____

I disagree because_____

_____

Drug Abuse

Activity C

Chapter 15

Name _____

Date _____ Period _____

Parents can help their teens make decisions about drugs. Pretend you are the parent of a teen. Complete the following exercises with the responses you would **want** your teen to give.

1. If I develop a problem of drug abuse, I can place the blame for this on

   _____ myself

   _____ my parents

   _____ my friends

   _____ society

2. Rank the following, indicating your answer to this statement: "I consider drug use most dangerous when…"

   Driving; at home alone; emotionally upset; with friends; at a party; at school

   Most dangerous _____

   _____

   _____

   _____

   _____

   _____

   Least dangerous _____

3. If you were at a party and knew drugs were being used by other people, what would you do?

   _____ leave immediately

   _____ stay at the party, but not use drugs

   _____ refuse drugs and try to tell the others they are wrong

   _____ try the drug just once out of curiosity

   _____ go along with the crowd, doing whatever they do

   _____ Other: _____

4. If a law were proposed making all drugs legal for anyone who wanted to use them, how would you vote?

   _____ make all drugs legal for everyone

   _____ make all drugs legal for people over 21

   _____ make marijuana legal, but restrict other drugs

   _____ make all drugs illegal

   _____ Other: _____

(Continued)

5. Place the letters in the blanks to indicate what you think are the most common reasons for drug use.

(A) low self-esteem (B) influence of friends (C) relief from pressures (D) boredom (E) rebellion of authority (F) pleasurable feeling of drug (G) started smoking cigarettes, which led to drugs (H) unable to say no to friends

Most common reason _____

_____

_____

_____

_____

_____

_____

_____ Least common reason

6. Place the letters in the blanks to rank the following, indicating your answer to this statement: "In my opinion, the most dangerous consequences of drug use are…"

(A) problems with the law (B) loss of ability to make responsible judgments (C) loud and boisterous actions (D) drowsy and lazy feelings (E) exaggerated emotions (F) loss of ability to drive safely (G) damage to physical health (H) possibility of becoming dependent on drugs (I) loss of parents' and other adults' respect (J) loss of self-respect

Most dangerous _____

_____

_____

_____

_____

_____

_____

_____ Least dangerous

7. How do you think parents should handle the issue of drugs with their teens? _____

_____

_____

_____

_____

_____

_____

_____

Communication About Sexuality

Activity D

Chapter 15

Name _____

Date _____ Period _____

Ideally, parents and their teens should be able to talk openly about sex. Suggestions for communication about sexuality are given below. Read each suggestion. Then describe what parents and teens can do to carry out these suggestions.

Suggestion	What Parents Can Do	What Teens Can Do
The channels of communication should be open.		
Factual information should be provided about teens' sexual and physical maturity.		
Teens should know how their parents feel about sexual issues and how parents developed these standards.		
Parents need to tell their teens about the risks of sexual activity.		
Other:		

Friendships and Dating

Activity E

Chapter 15

Name _____

Date _____ Period _____

Complete the following exercise about friendships and dating.

1. Friendships are of great importance to teens because _____

_____

_____

2. Parents should take a genuine interest in their teens' friends because_____

_____

_____

3. Teens sometimes need time to be alone because _____

_____

_____

4. Teens should have curfews.

   I agree because _____

   _____

   I disagree because_____

   _____

5. A fair curfew for a teen would be _____.

6. Teens should be allowed to date when they are _____ years old.

7. List topics parents and teens should discuss in relation to dating. _____

   _____

   _____

   _____

8. On an average date, a teen will probably spend $_____.

9. Teens should tell their parents all about their dates.

   I agree because _____

   _____

   I disagree because_____

   _____

10. Teens' social success depends on their dating relationships.

    I agree because _____

    _____

    I disagree because_____

    _____

Decision-Making Skills

Name _____

Date_____ Period _____

The decision-making process can help you make important decisions. Think of a decision you must make. Follow the steps in the decision-making process to determine the best alternative.

1. Identify the decision to be made.

_____

2. List three possible alternatives.

Option 1:_____

_____

Option 2:_____

_____

Option 3:_____

_____

3. Evaluate the alternatives by considering the consequences of each option. List the pros and cons below. Consider the present consequences as well as the long-term results of each option. Think about your personal priorities and the priorities of your family and others around you when weighing the alternatives.

Option 1:

Pros _____

_____

_____

_____

Cons _____

_____

_____

_____

Option 2:

Pros _____

_____

_____

_____

Cons _____

_____

_____

_____

(Continued)

Option 3:

Pros _____

_____

_____

_____

Cons _____

_____

_____

_____

4. Choose one alternative by reviewing the pros and cons of each option.

_____

_____

5. Act on the decision. List the steps you will follow in putting the plan into action.

A. _____

_____

B. _____

_____

C. _____

_____

D. _____

_____

6. Evaluate the results of your decision as soon as possible to determine the effectiveness of the decision-making process. Remember that you can learn from the results of every decision you make.

Building a Positive Self-Concept and Self-Esteem

Name _____

Date _____ Period _____

Read the suggestions below. Then give examples of how parents can help their teens build positive self-concepts and self-esteems.

Suggestion	Example
1. Parents should be specific in praise rather than using broad, general statements.	Instead of saying "You are always so helpful," say "I really appreciate your help in preparing dinner tonight."
2. Parents should remind their teens of past accomplishments. This may stimulate them to fulfill other accomplishments.	
3. Parents should tell their teens they love and care about them.	
4. Parents should give gestures of affection to their teens.	
5. Parents should listen to their teens with full attention and good eye contact.	
6. Parents should teach their teens social skills so they will feel confident when they are away from home.	
7. Parents should encourage their teens to eat nutritious meals and exercise to maintain healthy bodies.	
8. Parents should accept their teens for who they are, including strengths and weaknesses.	

Parents and Teens

Complete the statements about parents and teens by filling in the blanks using the words listed below.

generally	homes	secondary sex
self-concepts	puberty	decision making
bulimia nervosa	dates	guidelines
adolescence	hormonal	anorexia nervosa
binge eating disorder	self-esteem	school
abstractly		

_____ 1. _____ is a transitional time during which people graduate from the dependency of childhood to the independency of adulthood.

_____ 2. _____ is the process through which the body becomes capable of reproduction.

_____ 3. The beard growth and voice change in boys and the development of breasts and widening of hips in girls are _____ characteristics.

_____ 4. _____ is an eating disorder in which people voluntarily starve themselves.

_____ 5. _____ is an eating disorder often called the "binge-purge" syndrome.

_____ 6. _____ is a disorder in which persons overeat rapidly and routinely.

_____ 7. With the dramatic _____ and physical changes of adolescence, new feelings about sex may occur quite naturally.

_____ 8. Much of teens' intellectual development occurs at _____.

_____ 9. Teens' increased intellectual skills allow them to think better both _____ and _____.

_____ 10. Learning _____ skills is one of the most important aspects of teenagers' intellectual development.

_____ 11. The emotional development of teens is greatly affected by the emotional climate within their _____.

_____ 12. Parents should not feel guilty about setting definite _____ for the behavior of their teens.

_____ 13. Teens begin to attend social functions, first in group situations and then on individual _____, at different ages.

_____ 14. People's thoughts about themselves, or _____, change throughout their lives.

_____ 15. _____ is the positive or negative judgment people make about themselves.

16 Theories and Guidelines

Piaget

Activity A

Name _____

Chapter 16

Date _____ Period _____

Complete the following chart outlining Piaget's theory of intellectual development.

Stage	Age	Development
Sensorimotor stage: Step one Step two Step three Step four Step five Step six		
Preoperational stage		
Concrete operational stage		
Formal operational stage		

Erikson

Name _____

Date _____ Period _____

Complete the following chart outlining Erikson's theory of personality development.

Stage Sequence	Approximate Age	Step Toward Stable Personality	Description of How This Step Can Be Achieved
1			
2			
3			
4			
5			
6			
7			
8			

Freud

Activity C

Chapter 16

Name _____

Date _____ Period _____

Sigmund Freud developed a theory of personality development. This theory is based on three aspects of human functioning that Freud labeled the id, ego, and superego. Define each of these aspects and then give examples of how they are exhibited in children.

Id

Definition: _____

_____

Examples: _____

_____

_____

_____

_____

_____

_____

Ego

Definition: _____

_____

Examples: _____

_____

_____

_____

_____

_____

_____

_____

Superego

Definition: _____

_____

Examples: _____

_____

_____

_____

_____

_____

Maslow's Theory of Human Needs

Name _____

Date _____ Period _____

Complete the following chart using Maslow's theory to name human needs in order of their priority. Describe each level of need.

Need: _____

Description: _____

_____

_____

_____

Need: _____

Description: _____

_____

_____

_____

Need: _____

Description: _____

_____

_____

_____

Need: _____

Description: _____

_____

_____

_____

Need: _____

Description: _____

_____

_____

_____

Kohlberg

Name _____

Date _____ Period _____

Lawrence Kohlberg identified three levels of moral development. In your own words, describe each level and give examples of how parents can aid their children through the levels.

Preconventional Level:

Description: _____

_____

_____

_____

Examples: _____

_____

_____

_____

_____

Conventional Level:

Description: _____

_____

_____

_____

Examples: _____

_____

_____

_____

_____

Postconventional Level:

Description: _____

_____

_____

_____

Examples: _____

_____

_____

_____

_____

Theories and Guidelines

Name _____

Date _____ Period _____

Complete the statements below by filling in the blanks.

Piaget:

_____ 1. During the _____ stage, children learn about the world through their senses and body movements.

_____ 2. During the _____ stage, children learn by using language and mental images.

_____ 3. During the _____ _____ stage, children are increasingly able to resolve more complex problems and use basic logic.

_____ 4. During the _____ _____ stage, people can deal with more complex problems, finding several solutions and then choosing the most logical one.

Erikson:

_____ 5. Erikson described the establishment of a sense of basic _____ as the important task of the first years of life.

_____ 6. During the second stage, _____ versus shame, children learn to develop independence.

_____ 7. During the third stage, children develop a sense of _____ by putting their ideas into action.

_____ 8. During stage four, _____ children become capable and willing to make a productive effort.

_____ 9. During the fifth stage, people develop a healthy personal _____ on the positive side or role confusion on the negative side.

_____ 10. The sixth stage is a stage of _____ versus isolation.

_____ 11. During the seventh stage, _____ versus stagnation, people become concerned about their contributions to the world.

_____ 12. Stage eight, _____ versus despair, occurs when a person's major efforts are nearing completion.

Freud:

_____ 13. According to Freud, the _____ is the source of psychological and physical tension.

_____ 14. The _____ deals with logic and controlled behaviors.

_____ 15. The _____ is a person's moral code.

Maslow:

_____ 16. According to Maslow's theory of human needs, _____ needs have first priority.

_____ 17. The highest level of human needs according to Maslow is _____.

Kohlberg:

_____ 18. According to Kohlberg, young children in the _____ level behave in ways that allow them to avoid punishment or gain rewards.

_____ 19. At the _____ level, children's decisions are shaped by approval or disapproval from others.

_____ 20. At the _____ level, behaviors are based on more abstract principles of right and wrong, where a person develops a personal set of morals upon which decisions are based.

Parenting Strategies

Activity G

Chapter 16

Name _____

Date _____ Period _____

Complete the chart below, indicating the highlights of various parenting strategies programs.

Parenting Strategies and Author/Founder	Highlights
Active Parenting *Michael Popkin*	
Dreikurs' Doctrine *Rudolf Dreikurs of the Alfred Adler Institute in Chicago*	
P.E.T. (Parent Effectiveness Training) *Thomas Gordon*	
P.I.P. (Parent Involvement Program) *William Glasser*	
Responsive Parenting *Saf Lerman*	
S.T.E.P. (Systematic Training for Effective Parenting) *Don Dinkmeyer and Gary D. McKay*	
Toughlove *Phyllis and David York*	

Book Review

Name _____

Date _____ Period _____

Visit the library. Review a book written by a child specialist of your choice. Present your book review to the class.

Book: _____

Author: _____

Highlights: _____

_____

_____

_____

_____

_____

_____

_____

_____

_____

_____

Your opinion of this book: _____

_____

_____

_____

Would you recommend this book to parents? _____ Explain your answer. _____

_____

_____

_____

_____

_____

_____

_____

_____

17 Guiding Healthy Development

Guiding Children's Behavior

Activity A   Name _____

Chapter 17   Date_____ Period _____

Explain the meaning of each of the following concepts related to guidance and discipline. Then give an example to illustrate each concept.

1. Authoritarian parenting style:_____

_____

   Example: _____

_____

2. Permissive parenting style:_____

_____

   Example: _____

_____

3. Authoritative parenting style: _____

   Example: _____

_____

4. Positive reinforcement: _____

   Example: _____

_____

5. Negative reinforcement: _____

   Example:_____

_____

6. Natural consequences: _____

   Example:_____

_____

7. Logical consequences: _____

_____

   Example: _____

_____

8. Time out:_____

_____

   Example: _____

_____

Sibling Relationships

Name _____

Date _____ Period _____

The following phrases describe characteristics that are typical of oldest, middle, and youngest children in general. Decide which group of children each phrase describes. Then write *oldest*, *middle*, or *youngest* in the blanks.

_____ 1. Most independent

_____ 2. Often acts as the peacemaker within a family

_____ 3. May put forth extra effort to excel in a special skill

_____ 4. May seek a marriage partner who is capable of taking charge

_____ 5. Most likely to go to college

_____ 6. Receives a lot of bossing

_____ 7. Usually given more responsibility

_____ 8. Receives a lot of attention

_____ 9. Tends to be a good all-around student

_____ 10. As an adult, tends to be a calm, even-tempered marriage partner and parent

_____ 11. May be more pampered and less independent

_____ 12. Most self-confident

Explain why parents should concentrate on the strengths of each of their children as individuals.

_____

_____

_____

_____

_____

_____

_____

_____

_____

_____

_____

_____

_____

_____

_____

_____

_____

_____

Sibling Rivalry

Activity C

Chapter 17

Name _____

Date _____ Period _____

Read the suggestions below that describe how parents should deal with sibling rivalry among their children. Then give an example of how parents can follow each suggestion.

Suggestion	Example
1. Parents should include their children in some of the preparations for a new baby.	
2. Parents should try to give the older children special time alone with each parent as often as possible.	
3. Parents should recognize that each child has different needs and interests.	
4. Parents should not take sides in their children's quarrels. Instead, parents should acknowledge each child's feelings, and together they should solve the problem.	
5. Sometimes it is best for parents to let children settle their own disputes.	

Volunteer Work

Name _____

Date _____ Period _____

Answer the following questions regarding children and volunteer work.

1. What can children learn by doing volunteer work?

_____

_____

2. Explain why an employer might be more likely to hire a teen who has done volunteer work.

_____

_____

3. List and describe six volunteer projects you might encourage your children to pursue in the community if you were a parent. (Remember, the project should seem interesting and worthwhile to children.)

Project: _____

Description:_____

_____

_____

Project: _____

Description:_____

_____

_____

Project: _____

Description:_____

_____

_____

Project: _____

Description:_____

_____

_____

Project: _____

Description:_____

_____

_____

Project: _____

Description:_____

_____

_____

An Allowance

Name _____

Date _____ Period _____

Pretend you are a parent. You have decided to give your child an allowance. In the space below, describe your child. Then answer the following questions.

Child: Age— _____

Activities— _____

_____

_____

_____

1. What expenses should be covered by the allowance? _____

_____

_____

2. Why should a small amount of discretionary money be given to a child? _____

_____

_____

3. How much discretionary money should this child be given? Explain why. _____

_____

4. What other factors affect the amount of an allowance? _____

_____

_____

5. What amount would you consider a fair allowance for this child? _____

6. How often should the allowance be paid? _____

7. Would you keep back the allowance as a punishment? _____ Explain why. _____

_____

_____

8. Would you give the allowance in advance? _____ Explain why. _____

_____

_____

Money Values

Name _____

Date _____ Period _____

Pretend you are a parent. Complete the following statements about money values.

1. I (would/wouldn't) use an allowance system for my children because _____

_____

_____

_____

_____

2. I (would/wouldn't) use a "pay-by-the-job" system because _____

_____

_____

_____

_____

3. I (would/wouldn't) use a combination of systems because _____

_____

_____

_____

_____

4. I (would/wouldn't) simply give my children money when they need it because _____

_____

_____

_____

_____

5. Educating children about money is important because _____

_____

_____

_____

_____

_____

A Part-Time Job

Activity G   Name _____

Chapter 17   Date _____ Period _____

Interview a student who has a part-time job. Find out the answers to the following questions. Share your interview responses with the class.

Student:_____ Age: _____

Job and description: _____

_____

1. How many hours do you work per week? _____

2. What days do you work? _____

3. What are your hours? _____

4. How did you get this job? _____

5. What skills have you learned on your job? _____

_____

_____

6. What experiences provided by this job could you use in a future career? _____

_____

_____

7. Is your job challenging or boring? Explain._____

_____

_____

8. How does your job affect the time you spend on schoolwork?_____

_____

_____

9. Does your job conflict with special activities at school? Explain. _____

_____

_____

10. Does your job help you manage your time more efficiently? _____

_____

11. How does your job affect your social life? _____

_____

12. How does your job affect the amount of time you would spend with your family? _____

_____

_____

Children's Questions About Sex

Activity H

Name _____

Chapter 17

Date _____ Period _____

Pretend you are a parent. Write your response to the following questions asked by children of the following ages.

Ages 2-3: "Why are boys and girls different?" _____

_____

_____

_____

_____

Ages 3-4: "Where do babies come from?" _____

_____

_____

_____

_____

Age 4: "How does the baby get out?" _____

_____

_____

_____

_____

Ages 6-7: "How does a baby start to grow inside the mother?" _____

_____

_____

_____

_____

Explain why parents should not put off explanations to questions such as these by saying "We can't talk about that now." _____

_____

_____

_____

_____

Encouraging Honesty

Name _____

Date _____ Period _____

Ages of children and typical behaviors are listed below. Write a case study based on each of the following and suggest ways a parent could react. Discuss the case studies in class.

1. Age of child: 3

    Behavior: Telling tall tales

    Case study: _____

    _____

    _____

    _____

    _____

    _____

    Ways parents could react: _____

    _____

    _____

    _____

    _____

2. Age of child: 5

    Behavior: Lying

    Case study: _____

    _____

    _____

    _____

    _____

    Ways parents could react: _____

    _____

    _____

    _____

    _____

(Continued)

3. Age of child: 7

    Behavior: Child steals a toy from a store

    Case study: _____

    _____
    _____
    _____
    _____
    _____

    Ways parents could react: _____

    _____
    _____
    _____
    _____

4. Age of child: 15

    Behavior: Shoplifting

    Case study: _____

    _____
    _____
    _____
    _____
    _____

    Ways parents could react: _____

    _____
    _____
    _____
    _____

Television Influences

Name _____

Date _____ Period _____

In the space below, list what you consider to be the positive and negative effects of television on children. Then pretend you are a parent. List television viewing guidelines you would establish for your children. Discuss these guidelines in class.

Positive Effects of Television	Negative Effects of Television

Television viewing guidelines for your children: _____

_____

_____

_____

_____

_____

_____

_____

_____

_____

_____

_____

_____

_____

_____

(Continued)

Name _____

Pretend you are a parent. Name three current television programs. Describe why you would or would not allow your children to watch these programs.

Show #1: _____

Plot or purpose of the program: _____

_____

_____

_____

_____

I (would/wouldn't) allow my children to watch this program because _____

_____

_____

_____

_____

Show #2: _____

Plot or purpose of the program: _____

_____

_____

_____

I (would/wouldn't) allow my children to watch this program because _____

_____

_____

_____

_____

Show #3: _____

Plot or purpose of the program: _____

_____

_____

_____

I (would/wouldn't) allow my children to watch this program because _____

_____

_____

_____

18 Family Concerns

Dual-Career Households

Name _____

Date _____ Period _____

Indicate your opinion about the following statements concerning dual-career families. Use these statements as a basis for class discussion. (There are no right or wrong answers.)

Agree	Disagree	Unsure	
_____	_____	_____	1. For most parents, working is not an option but a necessity.
_____	_____	_____	2. In most dual-career families, men and women divide the household and child care tasks.
_____	_____	_____	3. Satisfaction as a marriage partner and a parent will be influenced by career satisfaction.
_____	_____	_____	4. It is not easy to balance multiple roles.
_____	_____	_____	5. People who are serious about their careers cannot manage their responsibilities at home as well.
_____	_____	_____	6. The success of a dual-career arrangement depends on the attitudes of both partners.
_____	_____	_____	7. If one mate does not want his or her spouse to work, continuous friction may cause problems in a dual-career household.
_____	_____	_____	8. It is unreasonable to expect an even division of all home tasks.
_____	_____	_____	9. Employers are becoming more willing to accommodate employees who must care for children.
_____	_____	_____	10. There are few differences between children of employed mothers and children of nonemployed mothers.
_____	_____	_____	11. When both parents work, children tend to be more independent and achievement-oriented.
_____	_____	_____	12. Children of working parents may be more social.
_____	_____	_____	13. Parents' attitudes toward work influence their children's feelings about work.
_____	_____	_____	14. Busy families may need to designate specific times to be together.
_____	_____	_____	15. Working couples may need to have more flexible housekeeping standards.
_____	_____	_____	16. The disadvantages outweigh the advantages in a dual-career household.
_____	_____	_____	17. Added income is the only advantage in a dual-career household.
_____	_____	_____	18. Children of dual-career families lack independence.
_____	_____	_____	19. Stay-at-home parents may be more likely to stifle their children's attempts at independence.
_____	_____	_____	20. Children of dual-career families are often more social.

Explaining Divorce to Children

Name _____

Date _____ Period _____

Complete the checklist by indicating your opinions about explaining divorce to children. Choose one statement with which you strongly agree and one with which you strongly disagree. Explain your reasoning and be prepared to discuss your reasoning in class.

Agree **Disagree**

_____ _____ 1. Parents should not worry children during the time they are thinking about getting a divorce.

_____ _____ 2. When the decision to divorce is final, parents should tell their children right away.

_____ _____ 3. The explanation of the divorce should come from only one parent.

_____ _____ 4. When breaking the news to children, parents should say one parent is just leaving on a vacation or a business trip.

_____ _____ 5. Parents should not give their children any reason to have false hopes of reconciliation.

_____ _____ 6. Throughout the divorce process, parents should treat each other with respect.

_____ _____ 7. The explanation of the divorce should come from both parents.

_____ _____ 8. Children need to be reassured they are still loved by both parents.

_____ _____ 9. Throughout the divorce process, parents should be hostile toward each other.

_____ _____ 10. Children should be used as weapons in the battle between parents.

_____ _____ 11. Both parents need to give truthful explanations of the present situation and future arrangements.

_____ _____ 12. Parents should not magnify each other's faults.

I strongly agree with statement _____ because _____

_____

_____

_____

_____

_____

I strongly disagree with statement _____ because _____

_____

_____

_____

_____

_____

_____

_____

Stepfamilies

Name _____

Date _____ Period _____

The stepfamily is becoming one of the most common family structures in the United States. Talk to members of stepfamilies or read current articles about stepfamilies. Then answer the following questions.

List the strengths of stepfamilies.

_____

_____

_____

_____

_____

List the challenges faced by stepfamilies.

_____

_____

_____

_____

_____

Describe ways these challenges might be met by members of stepfamilies.

_____

_____

_____

_____

_____

In your opinion, what is the major strength of stepfamilies? Explain why.

_____

_____

_____

_____

_____

In your opinion, what is the major challenge faced by stepfamilies? Explain why.

_____

_____

_____

_____

_____

An Illness in the Family

Name _____

Date _____ Period _____

Pretend a member of your family is ill. Design a greeting card ("Get Well," "Thinking of You," etc.) you could send to the person to show you care.

Describe the person and the illness: _____

_____

_____

Explain how the love and support of family members can help everyone cope during the illness of a family member.

_____

_____

Explaining Death to Children

Activity E   Name _____

Chapter 18   Date _____ Period _____

Complete the checklist by indicating your opinions about explaining death to children. Choose one statement with which you strongly agree and one with which you strongly disagree. Explain your reasoning and be prepared to discuss your reasoning in class.

Agree   Disagree

_____ _____ 1. Parents should avoid talking about death.

_____ _____ 2. Death should be treated as part of life.

_____ _____ 3. When a family experiences the crisis of death, parents should not shut out the children.

_____ _____ 4. Children should be allowed to grieve over the loss of a pet.

_____ _____ 5. Parents should immediately replace a dead pet with another one.

_____ _____ 6. Parents should be truthful when telling their children about death.

_____ _____ 7. Parents should say "Grandma has gone on a long trip."

_____ _____ 8. Parents should say "Grandpa has gone to the hospital."

_____ _____ 9. Parents should say "Grandma died because she was sick."

I strongly agree with statement _____ because _____

_____

_____

_____

_____

I strongly disagree with statement _____ because _____

_____

_____

_____

_____

If I were a parent, I (would/wouldn't) take my children to a grieving ritual such as a funeral or wake because __

_____

_____

_____

_____

_____

_____

_____

_____

_____

New in Town

Name _____

Date _____ Period _____

Interview a student or neighbor who has recently moved to your community. Find out the answers to the following questions.

1. What has been the most exciting aspect of your move? _____

_____

_____

2. What has been the most challenging aspect of your move? _____

_____

_____

3. Which members of your family have had the easiest time adjusting to the move? Why? _____

_____

_____

4. Which members of your family had more difficulty in adjusting to the move? Why? _____

_____

_____

5. What could people in the community do to make your adjustment easier? _____

_____

_____

6. How important is maintaining a positive attitude during the moving experience? _____

_____

_____

7. What do you miss most about your former community? _____

_____

_____

8. What do you look forward to since arriving in this community? _____

_____

_____

19 Family Crises

Help for Families Facing Financial Crises

Activity A

Chapter 19

Name _____

Date _____ Period _____

Investigate resources in your community that are available to help families in need. List each agency or service name and describe it.

Agency or Service	Description

Dealing with Substance Abuse Problems

Activity B

Chapter 19

Name _____

Date _____ Period _____

Read the following situations. Then describe how you think the family should handle each situation. Discuss your responses in class.

Situation	What Should Be Done?
1. Bill's mom has a drinking problem. Bill's dad and the rest of the family pretend she doesn't and try to ignore the problem.	
2. Shalonda's sister, Tracy, attends parties where drugs and alcohol are used. Shalonda cares about her sister and doesn't know what to do.	
3. Calvin doesn't like to bring his friends home. His dad is often drunk.	
4. Jane and Paul's daughter, Maria, is addicted to drugs. They do not want anyone to know someone in their family has a drug problem, so they try to cover up the situation and make excuses for Maria's actions.	
5. Kathy knows her teenage son, Scott, drinks alcohol. She hopes he will "grow out of it."	
6. Ken was arrested for drug possession. He is now in a rehabilitation program and will be returning to his family soon. His family is trying to cope with the situation.	

Child Abuse Laws and Programs

Activity C

Chapter 19

Name _____

Date _____ Period _____

Visit the library or contact local authorities to find answers to the following questions.

1. What are the laws in your state concerning child abuse? (List and briefly describe these laws.)

_____

_____

_____

_____

_____

_____

_____

_____

_____

_____

_____

_____

_____

_____

2. What local agencies or programs are available to help prevent child abuse? (List and describe these agencies or programs.)

_____

_____

_____

_____

_____

_____

_____

_____

_____

_____

_____

_____

_____

_____

_____

The Domestic Violence Cycle

Activity D

Chapter 19

Name _____

Date_____ Period _____

The three-phase cycle of domestic violence was described in the text. Fill in the diagram and complete the statements below.

The Three-Phase Cycle of Domestic Violence

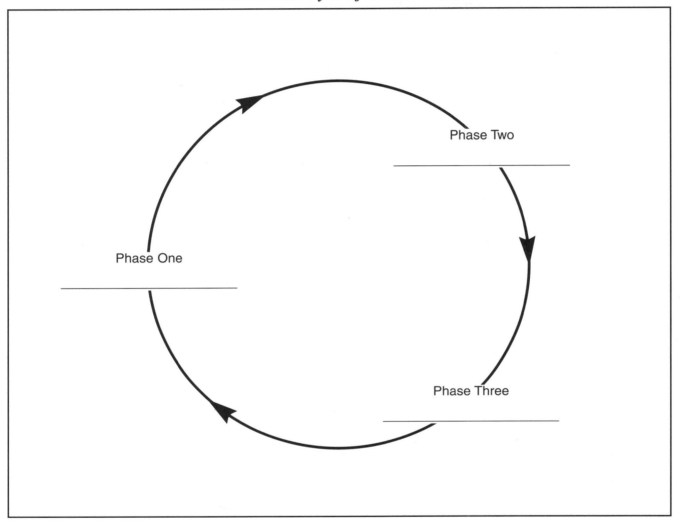

1. I believe a person who is a victim of domestic violence should _____

_____

_____

_____

2. In my community, victims of domestic violence can turn to_____

_____

_____

_____

_____

Gangs, Bullies, and Peer Violence

Activity E

Chapter 19

Name _____

Date _____ Period _____

Children who are victims of gangs, bullies, or peer violence often show signs they are being victimized. Read the following descriptions. If a statement describes a victim, write **V** in the blank. If the statement does not describe a victim, write **No** in the blank. Then answer the following questions.

Victims of bullying, gangs, or peer violence usually...

_____ 1. become depressed; have little self-esteem

_____ 2. are enthusiastic about school

_____ 3. have lots of friends

_____ 4. lose interest in schoolwork/activities; grades usually drop

_____ 5. become loners; shy away from friends

_____ 6. change in normal appetite

_____ 7. are seldom absent from school

_____ 8. wait to use the restroom until they arrive home

_____ 9. arrive home with torn clothes, unexplained bruises

_____ 10. have a good appetite

_____ 11. seem happy and well-adjusted

_____ 12. display anxiety about going to school, taking school trips, or participating in extracurricular activities

_____ 13. ask for extra money for school lunch, supplies, and extra allowance

_____ 14. seem confident

_____ 15. refuse to go to school

_____ 16. act moody, sullen, quiet; withdraw from family interaction

_____ 17. avoid going to certain areas in school or town

_____ 18. have trouble sleeping

_____ 19. participate in extracurricular activities

_____ 20. begin to carry self-protection weapons, such as a pocketknife

If your child were a victim of gangs, bullies, or peer violence, what would you do?

_____

_____

_____

_____

_____

_____

_____

Missing Children and Runaways

Activity F   Name _____

Chapter 19   Date _____ Period _____

Read the following statements about missing children and runaways. Indicate whether you agree or disagree with each statement by placing a check in the appropriate column. Discuss your responses in class.

Agree   Disagree

_____   _____   1. Parents should know where their children are at all times.

_____   _____   2. Parents may leave their children alone in the car as long as the car is locked.

_____   _____   3. Children should know their home phone number, including area code.

_____   _____   4. Parents should write their children's names on their clothes and books.

_____   _____   5. Children should be taught not to talk to strangers, ride with strangers, or get involved with strangers in any way.

_____   _____   6. Children should be fingerprinted for identification purposes.

_____   _____   7. When teens disagree with their parents, the best solution is for the teen to run away.

_____   _____   8. Running away usually compounds problems for teens.

_____   _____   9. Families left behind by runaways live in constant fear.

_____   _____   10. Teens who run away are likely to find the independence they seek.

I strongly agree with statement _____ because _____

_____

_____

_____

_____

I strongly disagree with statement _____ because _____

_____

_____

_____

_____

Preventing Teen Suicide

Name _____

Date _____ Period _____

The following factors and situations are listed by authorities as possible causes of suicide among teens. Suggest actions that might lead to a positive solution for each situation.

Factor/Situation	Solution
1. Lack of appreciation and understanding from family members	
2. Substance abuse problems	
3. Loss of a loved one	
4. Family has moved	
5. Emotional health problems	
6. Lack of a support system; feelings of isolation	

20 A Look at Child Care Options

Home-Based Child Care

Activity A   Name _____

Chapter 20   Date _____ Period _____

Visit a home where a child is given care in his or her home. You could also choose to visit a home where a child is given care in the caregiver's home. Briefly describe the arrangement. Then find out the following information.

Description of the home and the arrangement between the parents and the caregiver: _____

_____

_____

Adult-child ratio: _____ Ages of children: _____

Cost: _____

Describe a child's typical day with this caregiver. _____

_____

_____

_____

Describe the interaction between the caregiver and the child or children. _____

_____

_____

Are the meals and/or snacks nutritious? _____

Do the meals and/or snacks appeal to the child or children? _____

Is the home clean? _____

What safety precautions are followed? _____

_____

_____

If you were a parent, would you select this type of care for your child? _____

Explain. _____

_____

_____

_____

Child Care Centers

Activity B

Chapter 20

Name _____

Date _____ Period _____

Visit a child care center. Identify the type of center and describe it briefly. Then find out the following information.

Type of center:

_____ Government-sponsored   _____ University-linked

_____ Employer-sponsored (on-site)   _____ Privately-owned

_____ Cooperative   _____ Drop-in

_____ Play group   _____ Nationally-franchised

_____ Church-linked   _____ School-age

Description of center: _____

Adult-child ratio: _____ Ages of children: _____

Cost: _____

Describe a child's typical day at this center. (Describe the program.) _____

_____

_____

_____

_____

_____

_____

Describe the interaction between the caregivers and the children. _____

_____

_____

_____

_____

_____

_____

Are the meals and/or snacks nutritious? _____

Do the meals and/or snacks appeal to the children? _____

Is the center clean? _____

What safety precautions are followed? _____

_____

_____

_____

(Continued)

If you were a parent, would you select this center as child care for your child? Explain. _____

_____

_____

_____

_____

_____

_____

_____

_____

Specialized questions:

Government-Sponsored Child Care Center

Describe any additional licensing guidelines with which this center must comply. _____

_____

_____

_____

_____

_____

_____

_____

_____

_____

_____

_____

_____

Employer-Sponsored Child Care

Name of company: _____

List other local companies that provide employer-sponsored child care for the employee's children.

_____

_____

_____

_____

_____

(Continued)

Name _____

Describe various systems offered by these companies (on-site, "voucher system," "cafeteria style" benefits, etc.).

_____

_____

_____

_____

_____

_____

_____

How do companies benefit from helping provide child care for their employees' children? _____

_____

_____

_____

_____

_____

_____

_____

Cooperative Child Care or Play Groups

Describe the role of parents. _____

_____

_____

_____

_____

_____

_____

_____

_____

_____

_____

Evaluating a Child Care Program

Activity C

Chapter 20

Name _____

Date _____ Period _____

Visit a child care center. Evaluate the program at the center by answering the following questions. Compare your responses with those of class members who visited other centers.

1. Name of child care center: _____

2. Type of center: _____

3. Do parents have any input into the planning of the program? If so, how much and in what way?

   _____

   _____

4. Does the program appear to have a well-rounded selection of physical, intellectual, emotional, and social development activities?_____

   List examples of each:

   Physical— _____

   _____

   Intellectual— _____

   _____

   Social and emotional— _____

   _____

5. Is an area provided for creative activities?_____

6. Is a homemaking area provided? _____

7. Are musical instruments available? _____

8. Are reading skills encouraged through the use of reading circles and quiet reading areas?_____

9. Are age-appropriate computer programs available for children to use? _____

10. After comparing your evaluation with the evaluations of other class members who visited other centers, how would you rate the program of this child care center? *(Check one.)*

   _____ Excellent   _____ Good   _____ Fair   _____ Poor

Factors to Consider

Name _____

Date _____ Period _____

Parents choose child care facilities for different reasons. Factors parents may consider in making their choices are listed below. Pretend you are a parent. Rank these factors in order of importance to you. (Begin by writing the number 1 beside the most important factor.) Compare your rankings to those of other class members.

Factors to consider:

_____ location of facility

_____ program activities of child care center

_____ cleanliness of child care center

_____ cost of child care

_____ ratio of children per caregiver

_____ training and education of staff

_____ hours of operation

_____ transportation provided

_____ personal qualities of caregivers

_____ nutrition program

_____ equipment and supplies

_____ discipline methods used

_____ Other: _____

_____ Other: _____

Why did you choose _____

as the most important factor to consider?_____

_____

_____

Why did you choose _____

as the least important factor to consider? _____

_____

_____

Selecting Child Care

Name _____

Date _____ Period _____

Visit a child care center of your choice. Complete the following checklist. Total the number of checks marked in each column. Compare your checklist with those of other class members who visited other centers.

Yes   **No**

_____   _____   1. The care facility meets state, county, and city licensing requirements. It is checked regularly by authorities to see that certain standards are maintained.

_____   _____   2. The care facility has a good reputation.

_____   _____   3. The care facility is in a convenient location.

_____   _____   4. The cost for each child is reasonable.

_____   _____   5. Alternative schedules are available to meet various needs for hours per day and days per week.

_____   _____   6. The setting has a warm, homelike atmosphere.

_____   _____   7. The rooms and play areas are designed and decorated with children in mind.

_____   _____   8. The care facility is equipped with a variety of safe play equipment and arranged with safety in mind.

_____   _____   9. Precautions have been taken to prevent children from wandering away and strangers from entering the premises.

_____   _____   10. The restrooms are clean, easy for children to use, and in good condition.

_____   _____   11. The children have a comfortable and quiet place for naps.

_____   _____   12. There is an isolated place for an ill child.

_____   _____   13. Good emergency care is available for the children if the need arises.

_____   _____   14. The food is nutritious, well prepared, and suited to the age of the children.

_____   _____   15. The children are grouped according to age.

_____   _____   16. Suitable activities are planned for each age group.

_____   _____   17. Children are allowed to choose some of their own activities.

_____   _____   18. Children are allowed time for quiet individual play as well as active group play.

_____   _____   19. Each child is respected as an individual.

_____   _____   20. The needs of the parents are recognized by the caregivers.

_____   _____   21. The adult-child ratio is appropriate.

_____   _____   22. All areas of the care facility are supervised at all times.

_____   _____   23. If a child needs individual attention at times, it is available.

_____   _____   24. The caregivers are well trained and experienced.

_____   _____   25. Interactions between caregivers and children are pleasant.

_____   _____   26. The caregivers encourage the physical, intellectual, emotional, and social development of the children.

Name _____

Yes	No	
_____	_____	27. The caregivers attend promptly to children's needs.
_____	_____	28. The caregivers are calm, gentle, and fair to the children. They have a good sense of humor.
_____	_____	29. The caregivers discipline the children without the use of harsh punishment.
_____	_____	30. The children seem happy.
_____	_____	Totals

Additional notes: _____

_____

_____

_____

_____

_____

_____

_____

_____

_____

_____

After comparing your checklist to those of other class members, would you recommend this child care center to parents? _____ Explain your answer. _____

_____

_____

_____

_____

_____

_____

_____

21 Children's Education and Health

Using Teachable Moments

Activity A

Chapter 21

Name _____

Date _____ Period _____

Read the following situations. Work in a small group and discuss ways parents could use these situations as teachable moments with their children. In the space below, describe how parents could take advantage of these moments, combining the best ideas of the group members.

Situation	How Parents Can Take Advantage of This Teachable Moment
1. Four-year-old Nancy was watching her mother bake cookies. Her mother was cutting the cookie dough into different shapes. Nancy pointed to one of the cookies and said, "That's a star!"	
2. Leon and his father were sitting outside one evening. The moon was shining, and six-year-old Leon asked, "Daddy, where does the moon go in the daytime?"	
3. Five-year-old Cherie was picking flowers with her mother. She reached for a flower that was all dried up. She asked her mother, "Why is one flower so pretty and one flower so dry and brown?"	
4. Tommy and his dad went fishing. They saw a bird flying overhead. Tommy asked his dad, "Why can't a fish fly and a bird swim?"	
5. Amir and his mother walked by a house that was under construction. Amir asked, "How can they build a house that won't fall down?"	
6. Nine-year-old Sara was on vacation with her parents. She soon became bored with the long car ride. She said, "I wonder how many cars are from our state."	

Homework

Name _____

Date _____ Period _____

Agree   **Disagree**   **Unsure**

_____   _____   _____   1. Children who come from homes with clear structure, shared responsibilities, and set routines usually develop good study habits.

_____   _____   _____   2. Children from more permissive homes have more trouble accepting responsibility for their homework.

_____   _____   _____   3. Organizing and completing their homework helps children learn how to set priorities.

_____   _____   _____   4. Children's attitudes toward homework are largely affected by their parents' attitudes.

_____   _____   _____   5. Parents need to remind their children of their homework assignments.

_____   _____   _____   6. Use of positive reinforcement, such as praise, by parents can encourage their children to do their homework.

_____   _____   _____   7. Parents should do their children's homework for them.

_____   _____   _____   8. Parents should let their children know they are available to consult with them about their homework.

_____   _____   _____   9. Parents should talk with their children about special homework projects.

_____   _____   _____   10. Parents should suggest helpful resources for special projects and assist their children in finding resources.

I strongly (agree/disagree) with statement number _____ because _____

_____

_____

_____

_____

_____

_____

_____

_____

_____

_____

_____

_____

_____

_____

Current Developments in Education

Name _____

Date _____ Period _____

Find and read an article about new advances and current developments in educating one of the following types of children. Report your findings to the class.

Type of children: *(Check one.)*

_____ Children with mental disabilities

_____ Children with physical disabilities

_____ Children with learning disabilities

_____ Children with emotional disorders

_____ Gifted children

Title of article:_____

Source:_____

Report: _____

_____

_____

_____

_____

_____

_____

_____

_____

_____

_____

_____

_____

_____

_____

_____

_____

_____

_____

_____

_____

Education Crossword

Name _____

Date _____ Period _____

Across

1. _____ _____ is a condition that includes both significant subaverage general intellectual functioning and deficits in adaptive skills behavior.

4. The goal of education is to _____ and challenge children at each stage of their development.

6. The term _____ is used to describe any child who is outstanding in either a general sense or a specific ability.

8. Parents should make it clear they expect their children to meet all school responsibilities, including _____.

9. _____ means placing students of varying abilities in the same class.

10. Children with disabilities and children who are gifted are often called children with _____ needs.

Down

2. _____ _____ are spontaneous learning experiences that can be used to expand children's natural curiosity.

3. Ideally, learning _____ should be identified before children go to school.

5. _____ is as much the business of the home as of the school.

7. A person with an _____ disorder may not express feelings in acceptable ways for someone his or her age.

Children with Special Needs

Activity E

Chapter 21

Name _____

Date _____ Period _____

Interview the parents of a child with special needs. Find out the following information.

Description of the child: _____

_____

_____

_____

_____

Explain why this child is considered to have special needs. _____

_____

_____

_____

Describe the unique needs of this child. _____

_____

_____

_____

What special care or consideration does this child require?_____

_____

_____

_____

Describe the educational program(s) in which this child is involved. _____

_____

_____

_____

_____

_____

What are the challenges of raising a child with special needs? _____

_____

_____

_____

_____

_____

What are the rewards of raising a child with special needs? _____

_____

_____

_____

The Child Who Is Ill

Name _____

Date _____ Period _____

A child's behavior will change significantly when he or she becomes ill. Many times the first signs of illness are these changes in behavior. Write a short anecdote describing a child's behavior at the onset of an illness. Then describe some quiet activities you would introduce to the child during his or her recovery period.

Anecdote: _____

_____

_____

_____

_____

_____

_____

_____

_____

_____

_____

_____

_____

_____

_____

_____

_____

_____

Quiet activities for the recovery period: _____

_____

_____

_____

_____

_____

_____

_____

_____

_____

22 The Challenge of a Child and Family Services Career

Child-Related Career Opportunities

Activity A   Name _____

Chapter 22   Date _____ Period _____

In every community, rural and urban, there are many career opportunities in the child and family services field. Research the employment options in your community and answer the following questions.

1. List the options available in your community for part-time employment during high school in the child and family services field. _____

_____

_____

2. List six places of employment in your community with positions that involve working *directly* with children and families. Then list the job titles at each place of employment.

Place of Employment	**Job Titles**
A.	
B.	
C.	
D.	
E.	
F.	

3. Research one of the job titles you listed above. Describe what the position involves. Then list the qualifications necessary for that position.
   Job description: _____

   _____

   Qualifications: _____

   _____

4. List six positions in your community that involve working on behalf of children and families.

Place of Employment	**Job Titles**
A.	
B.	
C.	
D.	
E.	
F.	

(Continued)

5. Research one of the job titles you listed in number four. Describe what the position involves. Then list the qualifications necessary for that position.

Job description:_____

_____

_____

_____

_____

_____

Qualifications:_____

_____

6. List six positions in your community that involve creating and selling products and services for children.

Place of Employment	Job Titles
A.	
B.	
C.	
D.	
E.	
F.	

7. Research one of the job titles you listed in number six. Describe what the position involves. Then list the qualifications necessary for that position.

Job description:_____

_____

_____

_____

_____

_____

Qualifications:_____

_____

8. Which of the positions described above sound most interesting to you? Explain. _____

_____

_____

_____

_____

_____

_____

You Can Be an Entrepreneur!

Activity B

Chapter 22

Name _____

Date _____ Period _____

Many entrepreneurships involve working directly or on behalf of children and families. Others involve the creating and selling of products and services for children. In the following activity, brainstorm some ideas that might form the basis of an entrepreneurship. Then answer the remaining questions.

1. List several ideas for entrepreneurships related to children and families. If possible, think of some new ideas.

_____

_____

_____

Select one of the ideas you listed above that you feel has the greatest potential for success. Answer the following questions.

2. The idea with the most potential is _____

3. Explain why you feel this could be a successful business. _____

_____

_____

4. What do you see as the advantages of owning and operating this business? _____

_____

_____

5. What do you think the disadvantages would be? _____

_____

_____

6. What skills would you need to operate a business like this? _____

_____

_____

7. What resources would you need to start this business (money, equipment, supplies, etc.)? _____

_____

_____

_____

_____

8. Do you think you would want to be an entrepreneur? Explain your answer. _____

_____

_____

_____

_____

Interests, Aptitudes, and Abilities

Chapter 22   Name _____

Activity C   Date _____Period _____

Knowing what your interests, aptitudes, and abilities are can help you to find a fulfilling career. Perform a self-assessment by answering the questions below.

1. What are your interests? (Interests are activities that appeal to you.)

   _____

   _____

   _____

   _____

2. What are your aptitudes? (Aptitudes are your natural talents.)

   _____

   _____

   _____

   _____

3. What are your present abilities, and what abilities can you develop? (Abilities are skills that have been learned or developed.)

   _____

   _____

   _____

   _____

4. Describe a career you might want to pursue.

   _____

   _____

   _____

   _____

5. How might the interests, aptitudes, and abilities you have listed above be useful to you in that career?

   _____

   _____

   _____

   _____

Personal Characteristics

Name _____

Date _____ Period _____

Many of the personal characteristics needed to be a good parent are similar to those needed to succeed in a career. A variety of personal characteristics are listed to the left below. Number the five characteristics you feel are necessary to be a good parent, with 1 being the most important. In the next three columns, indicate (in order of importance) the five characteristics you feel are needed for success in each of these career areas. Then write a paragraph evaluating the similarities and differences in the four columns.

Personal Characteristics:	Parents	Working Directly with Children	Working Indirectly with Children	Creating and Selling
Patient				
Honest				
Loving				
Disciplined				
Enthusiastic				
Sense of humor				
Dependable				
Willing to listen				
Creative				
Self-motivated				
Compassionate				
Cooperative				
Adaptable				
Courteous				
Determined				

_____

_____

_____

_____

_____

_____

_____

_____

_____

_____

_____

_____

Trends in Child Care Careers

Activity E

Chapter 22

Name _____

Date _____ Period _____

Interview someone who employs child care workers. Compare your interview responses to those of others in the class.

Person interviewed: _____

Person's title: _____

Location: _____

1. Describe the demand for child care providers in this area. _____

_____

_____

_____

2. Do you recruit and hire employees with the CDA (Child Development Associate) Credential? Why or why not?

_____

_____

3. Is this center or home accredited? Why or why not?_____

_____

_____

4. Does this center place an emphasis on early childhood education? (If so, please describe the curriculum.)

_____

_____

5. Does this center provide special education programs? (If so, please describe the programs.) _____

_____

_____

6. Do staff members belong to professional organizations related to child care? If so, which ones?_____

_____

_____

7. What trends do you see taking place in the child care field?_____

_____

_____

8. What trends would you like to see take place in the child care field?_____

_____

_____

List three overall trends you noted after comparing interview responses with those of others in the class.

_____

_____

_____

Developing Leadership Skills

Name _____

Date _____ Period _____

The leadership skills you develop in school will be very valuable to you in the career world. In the following activity, list ten characteristics of a good leader. Then evaluate your leadership skills using this list. Rate each leadership skill on a scale of 0 to 5 with 5 being the highest. Total your score. Then answer the remaining questions.

Characteristics of a Good Leader:	Your Rating:
1.	
2.	
3.	
4.	
5.	
6.	
7.	
8.	
9.	
10.	
	Total:

1. How can you improve your leadership skills? _____

_____

_____

2. Select a student organization that interests you. Evaluate the leadership opportunities this organization can provide.

Name of organization: _____

Leadership opportunities: _____

_____

_____

_____

_____

_____

_____

_____

_____

_____

_____

Your Resume Worksheet

Activity G

Chapter 22

Name _____

Date _____ Period _____

Create your own resume by filling in the following information about yourself. You may wish to refer to your text for an explanation of each item.

Name: _____

Address: _____   Phone:_____

_____

Education   _____

_____

_____

_____

_____

_____

Work Experience   _____

_____

_____

_____

_____

_____

Special Skills   _____

_____

_____

_____

_____

_____

Activities   _____

_____

_____

_____

_____

References available upon request.